Contents

KT-237-791

Foreword

by Barbara Pointon

Dementia will soon touch every family in the land. Whether you are a person with dementia, a professional, a family member or an interested friend, this book is a 'must read'.

I found the hardest part of caring for my husband Malcolm was the period of trying to cope with perplexing, sometimes downright bizarre behaviours and uncharacteristic aggression. Like many others in this book, at first I unfairly labelled him as 'attention-seeking' or 'deliberately provocative' and attributed it to his dementia causing a personality change. Had this book been in my hands then, I would have understood much more about what was causing these strange behaviours, and I would have done many things differently, to the benefit of both of us.

Through 22 moving stories of real people in real circumstances, sensitively told, Graham Stokes provides many fascinating insights into what often appears to us as the topsy-turvy world of dementia. Like a shrewd detective picking up on clues (often long-buried in the past) he gradually uncovers the reasons which lie behind the behaviours or emotions of an individual and suddenly they make sense. Equally important, that new understanding provides the essential key to help carers devise imaginative and successful ways of dealing with the situation. And throughout, Dr Stokes' thoughtful and respectful attitude towards the person with dementia and members of their family forms a lesson in itself.

Another important theme which runs like a red thread through the book is that of well-intentioned but totally inappropriate, even malign care. Meet the damaging world of control (and I confess how easy it is to step over that fine line between caring and controlling), of rigid institutional routines, of risk avoidance, of unhelpful environments, of eagerness to prescribe or run for the sedatives, of attributing everything to dementia, of mechanistic caregiving, of one size fits all.

Yet time and again the author's message rings out that every person is unique and remains true to themselves. He also shows how changing the hearts and minds of caregivers results in truly person-centred care. Gaining better knowledge and understanding of the factors influencing behaviours and emotions transforms attitudes and fosters greater sensitivity, thoughtfulness and empathy towards the individual.

That's good news for the person with dementia and also for their family and professional caregivers whether at home or in care homes. They may well find this part of their job becomes less stressful and be encouraged to carry on caring for longer. And the wider world becomes wiser about what it means to live with dementia.

Each poignant story has so much to teach. This is a book which will change lives.

Introduction

*A*nd *Still the Music Plays* grew out of my increasing wish to say more. A few years ago I wrote an acknowledgement dedicating a book to the men and women with dementia whom it had been my privilege to meet. I valued the time they had given to share their experiences and talk about their lives and how we had faced many struggles and had to negotiate occasional exasperation. These were the people who helped to radically change our understanding of dementia. The knowledge that neuropathology does not, and never did, explain everything was not uncovered in the laboratory, it was not the product of an elegant medical breakthrough – it came about through appreciating the struggles of people attempting to live their lives in the face of terrible brain diseases that progressively destroyed their ability to remember, speak, understand and reason.

What has become known as the 'person-centred' model of dementia is founded on the experiences of people who never knew that one day they would be afflicted by a condition that would ultimately blight their lives. You would not need to turn the clock back more than a few short years to find a person who was like us in every way, shape and form, enjoying the same pleasures as we do, facing the same daily trials as our own, blissfully ignorant of the fact that before too long they were to be diagnosed with dementia. They had done nothing wrong, they did not deserve it, nor were they peculiar in any way. They were like you and me, and then seemingly inexplicably they were struck down. This book is about these people. Stories about who they were, who they remain and the difficulties they faced. Extraordinary stories about ordinary people.

I came across Grace, Colin, Mrs S, Patrick, Sylvia, Jack and all those whose stories are told in this book in many different settings – in hospital, in their own houses, living in care homes, or attending day centres. Some I got to know through their families and carers, while others became known to me after they had been referred to my clinic. One I even got to know beyond the grave! For some I was there in the early days as tiny inexplicable changes started to gather momentum and cause increasing worry, while for others I arrived late and I was only there at a time of advanced illness when my words were barely understood and within moments of me leaving I had never existed.

And Still the Music Plays comprises three sections. The first, 'From Beginnings to Endings' recounts the stories of six people from the early days of their dementia. This is a time of unfolding fears and eventual all-encompassing dread, but also a time of human acts that are a testimony to the strength and fortitude of the human spirit when faced with what one of them called "this dementia thing". 'Challenges as Windows' looks at the uniqueness of people and how their efforts to be true to themselves took them down paths that led them to be seen as challenging, behaving in such outlandish and bizarre ways they were seen as strangers, and the tolerance of others was stretched to breaking point. The final part, 'The Good, The Bad and The Indifferent', is both despairing and uplifting. Despairing because of the insensitivity people with dementia can still be exposed to as their vulnerability increases and they are more and more dependent on other people to give them peace of mind and a reason to be alive. Uplifting when compassion and creativity shine like beacons and the lives of people with dementia are valued and consequently transformed. Hence this section is not devoid of that most exacting of human emotions – hope, for a glimpse of what was possible was never far away. Perseverance and commitment were needed to under-stand the inner fractured world of people facing, on occasions, torment beyond belief.

I hope these stories bring to life the experiences of these wonderful people. We are all, like them, complex and fascinating individuals. And therein lies a lesson. None of these people knew their destiny. Not one knew what was to befall them. From the moment I met them or in those instances when the dementia was all-consuming, as their stories became known it was their normality that impressed me. So, who among us will also embark upon the same journey? One day these stories could be ours.

Graham Stokes, January 2008

PART I

From beginnings to endings

"Publish such histories, even if they are just sketches. It is a realm of great wonder."
– A R LURIA

ONE

"I need my list..."

Grace was a woman of distinction. Not to the world at large, perhaps, but certainly to her husband and sons. Her friends admired how she had encouraged her husband Phil, once a gas fitter, to fulfil his ambition to run his own business. He could set his hand to anything practical and over the years he had renovated and extended their end of terrace cottage. It was Grace who said, "Do it. You're fed up. You know you want to work for yourself. What's the worst that could happen? We find out you're not a businessman. That wouldn't be the end of the world. There'll always be a job for you." So, fortified with the knowledge that Grace had faith in him, Phil found the confidence to start up his own building firm.

The worst that happened was that in the early days, of which they agreed there were too many, the business was slow to flourish. Grace had to work part-time in a super-market as well as bring up their two sons, who in the local vernacular could be a couple of 'lovable scallies'. She also found out that Phil was not the most organised when it came to paperwork. Nor was he at his best when it came to saying no. He often had too many jobs on the go. He could get so overstretched that invoices, the cheques that needed to be in their account and not left in an envelope, the orders for materials, the bills to be paid, the calls to be returned... well, they would all have to look after themselves.

Grace came to the rescue. She didn't simply organise the office, she created it, managed it and made sure that Phil could do what he did best – build. She had found out that he was not a businessman. But there would be no regrets. She stepped into the breach and became the unsung hero who made sure that all ran smoothly, just as she had done when bringing up the boys. She told them that one day they no longer would be seen simply as mischievous and if they did not mend their ways others might not find them so easy to forgive. They had listened, learnt some tough lessons and, now aged 17 and 19 years old, started working for their father. While the men of the house built with bricks and mortar, Grace had built the family in her own image – caring, industrious and determined.

Phil could not say precisely when he knew, but slowly it dawned on him that things were not as they should be. Unpaid bills were lying around, cheques weren't always paid in and letters were left unopened. Phil couldn't find what he needed. The bank rang asking if he needed to increase his overdraft limit on his business account, and if he did was he having problems with his cash flow? Would it be possible for him to call in for a talk? Phil, stressed as ever, was not best pleased. Peculiarly, Grace seemed unaware of the problems, didn't appreciate that she was forgetting what she said she would do, and, even more perplexing, seemed not to grasp the significance of what was happening.

Matters went from bad to worse. Grace was not only unable to remedy the increasingly chaotic office, she was not herself. She had lost her sparkle. She was distracted. At times she was irritable. She just wasn't Grace.

One day, consumed with worry to the point that he could no longer lose himself in his work, and with his sons pestering him to "do something about mum", he made an appointment for Grace to see their GP. On the day of the appointment he didn't know what he would say. Was he being silly? This wasn't for a doctor to hear. Maybe he had taken Grace for granted. She just needed a holiday, or maybe he could do more to help. Maybe for too long they had all been guilty of always assuming that "Mum'll do it".

Grace had agreed to go, even though she didn't know why they were all making such a fuss. She was just tired. The doctor asked what was wrong, but Grace said nothing. Phil said that she wasn't herself. It wasn't that she couldn't cope, it was more that she didn't seem to care. She was often withdrawn. Even on the odd occasion when she was more like her old self, Phil thought that his wife didn't always concentrate on what was going on. She would lose track of conversations and could say the wrong thing. Hearing that this had been going on for a few months, and knowing how much Grace had taken on over the years, her GP was sure the problem was one of depression. He prescribed a course of anti-depressants and said he would follow her up in a month.

A month later Phil told the GP that he thought there had been a slight improvement, but wasn't certain. Grace again said little. The decision was taken for her to continue with the anti-depressants for another month. The GP said it was just a precaution, more routine than anything else, but he would also like her to have a blood test.

When they found themselves next with their GP, Phil was confident all was well. Grace, while not saying so herself was definitely more like her normal self. During the consultation she was for the first time talkative. They were both pleased to hear that the blood test was normal. Grace's mood had definitely lifted. Phil talked of her being more active around the house and, reassuringly, for him in the office as well. Things were not as they once were, but everything was going in the right direction. As she talked, admitting that things had got on top of her and how she felt that she had been letting everybody down, the conversation betrayed a continuing failing. Occasionally she would trip up over a word, at another time she repeated herself. Nothing dramatic, just unexpected. It was a surprise to both of them when the doctor said he wanted to refer Grace to the hospital so a consultant physician could see her. He was reasonably confidant there was nothing wrong, but it made sense to be sure. In his notes the GP wrote: "Signs of improvement. Memory still not normal. Poss. speech problems. Alzheimer's disease? Unlikely. Refer."

The investigations were exhaustive and to Phil and Grace reassuring. Nothing was found to be wrong but the consultant did not share their optimism. He wanted Grace to have a brain scan. The results were like all the others – normal, yet still the consultant was not happy. He talked about referring Grace to a neuropsychologist.

At this point Phil lost it. He demanded to know what was going on. For the first time dementia was disclosed as a possible diagnosis. While the physical investigations were all negative this meant that they didn't have an explanation as to why Grace's memory was not how it should be. There had been improvement, but Phil had to admit that he did keep a watchful eye on his wife when before he would never even have contemplated doing so, and yes she still did make silly mistakes, even though these were now infrequent. As he said, "she can be really unGrace-like". And had he not noticed how she occasionally used the wrong words in conversation? He admitted he had. Now Phil knew why he had been asked during that first meeting with the consultant, "has anybody in your wife's family suffered from Alzheimer's disease?" He had said no, and surely this couldn't be the explanation. Dementia? It couldn't be, that happened to old people. Grace was only 41 years old!

When I first met Grace there was little to suggest that much was wrong. She was courteous and bubbly. Life was on an even keel. She readily joined in the assessments. There was the odd error, in particular when testing her reasoning (on a standard clock drawing test she hesitated when setting the hands of the clock to '10 past 11', her pencil seemingly being pulled to the number '10', and she took a long time working out '10.45'), and when examining her memory when she was not expecting it (testing what is known as *incidental learning*). In all other areas of thinking, language and remembering she tested reasonably well. Yet after each examination I was left feeling uneasy. The few errors and inconsistencies that would surface, as well as the fluctuations as the months passed made little sense. One day I asked Grace to plan a route on a map so she would end up visiting places of interest in a set sequence. She suddenly appeared fragile and uneasy, as if I had tapped into a well of inadequacy. She abruptly stopped, saying she had better things to do than play games. Composing herself within moments she apologised and headed back to the safe ground of asking whether I wanted a cup of coffee, for in daily life Grace was functioning not only well, she was continuing to improve and surprise. Yes, she was more cautious, less confident but the nadir of several months ago was becoming a distant memory. However, Phil was far from satisfied. He still wanted to know "what the hell was going on".

Phil had been frightened witless having been told that it was possible his wife was suffering from Alzheimer's disease. He had surfed the internet, getting reams of information. He knew what to expect. The degradation. The loss of shared moments. No longer would they have a relationship. She would not even recognise him. She would remember nothing of what they had achieved. What about the boys? How would they cope seeing their mother taken away from them in this way? What about him, how would he cope? And yet now, Grace was getting better. That would be impossible if she had Alzheimer's disease. You don't recover from dementia. At times he found it difficult to control his feelings. Exasperated, he would say, "Will you guys get your f***ing act together and tell us what is going on?" Grace would try and calm him, but he was right: what was going on? Grace was better than she was and doing well, but it didn't feel right. I would talk with Phil and agree that she had improved to the point that he was now able to rely on her again, but I would say, "Phil, I can't disagree, things are better and I know that isn't what we expected, but you must understand we are still having some pretty unusual conversations. We talk about whether Grace is safe to go out by herself. You don't have conversations like that when talking about somebody who is your wife's age unless something is wrong." But what?

Just before Christmas Grace met with Suzie, one of the junior members of the team with whom she had an especially good relationship. If possible, an assessment should never feel like an examination – it is just two people talking with one trying to learn as much as they can about the other. As they sat together in Grace's lounge I don't know why Grace chose to drop her defences, but she did. Intriguingly she said, "I'm making the best of it." What could Suzie, say, other than, what do you mean? And so Grace's story unfolded.

She was coping well, but nobody realised the time, effort and ingenuity she invested in doing so. Her husband and the boys would be up and out by 6.30 every morning, so at night she would be the last to bed. It was she who would close down the house. She would turn out the lights, make sure the doors were locked and write her list – the list she needed to get through the next day.

Now many of us may rely on lists -'jobs to be done'-
but not one like Grace's. She would discreetly place it on
the side of the fridge with a magnet. She would then set the
alarm on the small clock she kept hidden behind the CD
player on top of the fridge. And then with peace of mind
that she was still coping she would go to bed. The next
morning, added to the noise of the radio, washing machine
and whatever else that constituted a typical early morning
for Grace, would be the shrill of an alarm ringing. This was
the signal to check her list and stop all else:

8.45am Re-set alarm to 9.00a.m. Pin list to inside of
front door. Get ready to go out.
9.00am The alarm was Grace's cue to head to the front
door. And there again would be the list she needed:
"Ready to leave? Are any taps running? <u>Checked.</u>
Everything switched off? <u>Checked.</u> Is the back door
locked? <u>Checked.</u> Check make-up in mirror. Check
shoes. Put coat on. Need bag, purse and keys. <u>Make
sure.</u> Leave house. TAKE LIST WITH YOU. KEEP
IN BAG.
• Remember names. Lucy (no.24). Alison (no.22)
• Cross road. Turn left. At end of road turn right. Wait
  at bus stop. Number 17 bus.
• Count six bus stops. Get off. Wait for bus to pull
  away. Cross road. Go into bank. Pay in...
  CROSS OFF.
• Out of bank. Pause. Turn right. Three shops down is
  the chemist. We need... CROSS OFF.
• Out of chemist. Cross road. Into precinct. Into
  supermarket. We need... CROSS OFF.

- Walk out of precinct. Cross road. Turn left. Walk past the parade of shops. Bus stop. Number 17 bus.
- Count six bus stops. Get off. Wait for bus to pull away. Cross road. Turn right. Turn left – Manor Avenue. Walk down. Cross road. We live at no. 26 (red gate)."

And in she walked. Phil and the boys would bombard her with questions. Yes, she had been to the bank. Cheques were all paid in and she had asked for the balance on the account. No she hadn't forgotten to go to the chemist. And for dinner tonight she had bought as a surprise... This is how she coped. Without her list Grace knew that more than likely she would not even have got on the right bus, let alone known what to do when she had arrived in town. She lived on her wits. If something needed to be done she would do it. Never put it off. Routines were important. She had a place for everything, and everything was in its place. All around the home she had notepads, as well as a calendar and a clock in every room. Information always ready to hand. Nobody noticed, for aren't we all so busy with our own lives to take much notice of the minutiae that are around us? It was why the newspaper was always open on the table in the lounge. It not only gave her immediate access to the day and date, but there was always something to talk about.

The kitchen had been a problem for her. Grace realised this when making beans on toast one evening. She had the slices of bread. She had opened the tin of beans. She put the baked beans on the bread and then attempted to put it all into the toaster! Problems of concentration and logical reasoning were now hurdles to overcome, and she did. She may now have to rely more on prepared meals, sauces and seasoning mixes. But the choice was huge and she could keep a secret. What woman didn't add to her culinary talents by taking the occasional short cut? Grace simply took more. So Phil still got his sausages and mash with onion gravy, not knowing that it was instant mashed potato and a gravy mix. As Grace said, if she tried to make mashed potato she would do something silly – forget to put water in the saucepan, let the saucepan boil dry, even forget to peel the potatoes. She knew there were certain battles you do not fight, and there were others you do, because you might just win.

Progressively deprived of her ability to remember, Grace had transcended its loss with the same fortitude that she had always displayed. We are all resourceful in different ways, and some of us will always be better equipped to cope with dementia than others. On a journey "from familiarity and certainty to uncertainty; the whole underpinned by helplessness and fear" (in the words of John Keady and colleagues, writing in the *Journal of Dementia Care*), Grace's spirit had again been liberated, this time by dementia. Deprived of what we take for granted, Grace had again achieved rare humour, valour and resilience of spirit despite being, or maybe because she was, afflicted with Alzheimer's disease.

&

TWO

A man and his legacy

Was it Mr Abrahams' sixth sense that led him to make such an important decision? Was he haunted by the vision of what was to come and so knew he had to put matters right? I do not know, because I never met Stanley Abrahams.

Towards the end of 1991 Mr Abrahams had a fall, by all accounts a nasty one, while tidying his garden. The day after, his wife noticed that his tendency to forget had worsened. He would lose concentration when talking or watching television more often than before. At times he could be "very confused". What his wife had been aware of for nearly three years had suddenly got much worse. Mr Abrahams' doctor decided to refer him to the nearby teaching hospital for a specialist assessment.

Between February and March 1992 Mr Abrahams was rigorously examined. It was noted that he was a pleasant and cheery man who was managing well in everyday life. He *"still makes morning tea and can cope with his PIN number and burglar alarm. He is still driving and his wife says his driving is fine. His wife says that she is gradually taking over form filling. He has no problems in managing personal care although he is gradually reducing the number of tasks he can do about the house".*

Formal cognitive assessment yielded evidence of mild to moderate impairment. The consultant psychiatrist wrote in the notes *"memory difficulties – short term"*, *"difficulty in finding words and completing sentences, but comprehension probably intact"*. At the end of the assessment period, Mr Abrahams' polite and pleasant personality was again felt worthy of mention.

A CT scan of brain revealed evidence of atrophy (the wasting and loss of brain cells). The psychiatrist's diagnosis was *"senile dementia of the Alzheimer type"*. She recommended Mr Abrahams stop driving and his wife take out an Enduring Power of Attorney to manage his financial and legal affairs. This couple were now to embark upon a journey they had never contemplated to a destination they would never have wished to visit.

Two months after the diagnosis, Mr Abrahams' doctor observed that his *"mental functioning was deteriorating"* and that he was *"particularly handicapped by his poor short-term memory"*. A community psychiatric nurse started to visit. In July Mr Abrahams returned to the out-patient clinic and it was noted that he had become more disorientated. It was at this time that he reluctantly stopped driving. By December his GP was concerned that his wife, who was not in good health, was struggling to cope. Mr Abrahams had started *"wandering in the evening. He will occasionally go upstairs and pack a bag and head off for the railway station. Thus far he has always returned..."* The GP requested an urgent psychiatric opinion. Three days before Christmas, a psychiatrist visited. Again the picture was of a *"well-dressed man. Friendly manner".* The extent of his deterioration was determined by his inability to respond to any of the test questions, although it was noted that he was still able to follow simple instructions.

Five months later Mr Abrahams was described as *"helpless, demented and disoriented... is increasingly wandering away from home".* The following day he was admitted to hospital for assessment. In truth his admission was prompted by his wife's exhaustion. Despite the severity of his dementia a theme recurs in the admission record. *"Social skills retained... Elegantly dressed in a navy suit. Very friendly with exquisite manners... polite... Very pleasant and co-operative. However, responses to all questions rambling and meaningless and entirely inappropriate. His present problem is he wanders off at night. Can't recognise his wife or his house. His wife has to remain awake to keep him in. She is finding it difficult to cope."*

While the intellectual changes were profound, there was much about Mr Abrahams that endured and survived. If he was 'held' in the social moment he appeared a different man altogether compared to the one who was descending into the intellectual abyss of nothingness when there were things to be remembered and tasks to be done. In the company of others, even strangers, Mr Abrahams thrived. He was able to be himself, for if a single expression depicts the character of

22

Mr Abrahams it was 'hail fellow, well met'. This congenial man came alive when touched by human contact. Perhaps here is a lesson. However great the intellectual dissolution in dementia, there remains the undiminished possibility that we can touch the essence of a person, their human spirit, for as Oliver Sacks wrote in *The Man Who Mistook his Wife for a Hat*, this "can be preserved in what seems at first a hopeless state of neurological impairment".

How would Mr Abrahams now fare in hospital? Would others stay in touch with the essence of this appealing and sociable man?

Mr Abrahams spent the next five weeks in hospital. He was then discharged to an EMI (elderly mentally infirm) nursing home. The contents of the discharge letter were a testimony to who he had become: *"appearance has deteriorated, and he looks haggard... He will do bizarre things... Occasionally he will get physically aggressive. He is incontinent of urine"*. In the space of 35 days, what had happened to this courteous, elegantly dressed man with exquisite manners who had walked onto the ward in the company of his wife?

In the year since the diagnosis, Mr Abrahams' deterioration had been rapid. It was felt this was probably due in part to him having also suffered 'mini-strokes'. But what had caused the catastrophic destruction of all that was known about Mr Abrahams' personality during his short stay on the assessment ward?

As I examined the nursing notes, the serious shortcomings that were to characterise his time in hospital began to surface within hours of his arrival on the ward: no evidence of cruelty and neglect, but signs of insensitivity, thoughtlessness and an inability to empathise with his experiences. This dehumanising and unfeeling world of care, often driven by good intentions, was described by the influential dementia academic Tom Kitwood as a 'malignant social psychology'.

At first he kept himself to himself in his bedroom. During the afternoon he was discovered smoking a couple of times: *"It was explained to Stanley that he should not be smoking in his room because of fire risk and to approach a member of staff whenever he wants to smoke, so that he could be shown where he should smoke. He said, 'I've always smoked where I wanted to'. Managed to remove lighter from his possession which is kept in office drawer to be given to him when he wants to smoke. Refused to eat supper."* While the intentions can be understood and respected, they were talking to a man who could not remember words and experience for more than a few seconds. How long do we need to contemplate before we appreciate how he must have felt? And the cigarette lighter? It had been a present from his wife, given to him 24 years earlier on his 50th birthday.

The following day Mr Abrahams became agitated. He put his hat and coat on several times and packed his bag, saying he wished to leave. To calm him he was prescribed Haloperidol, a major tranquilliser, also known as an anti-psychotic. Unfortunately he became more and more restless as the day progressed: *"Trying to leave the ward. Is able to open both doors to the ward. Had to be stopped from doing so several times. Prescribed medication given with very little effect."* His wife telephoned and told them that she had spent many hours sitting and walking with her husband consoling and reassuring him. She was told that staff did not have the time to do this. Mrs Abrahams was *"advised not to visit for he remains very restless and at times adamant that he must leave"*. Contrary to what was known about his wife's ability to soothe him, it was felt her presence would encourage him even more to leave the ward.

This pattern of behaviour continued to evolve over the next couple of days. When he was admitted, Mr Abrahams was assessed to have *"complete orientation with prompting or reminders"*; within 48 hours his orientation was assessed as *"incomplete. Unable to accept or reject explanations"*. After his meals he would try to leave the ward. At night he would take his clothes in and out of his room. However, on a day that his wife visited, *"he was less agitated this afternoon and not packing his clothes to leave. His wife has brought in some treats"*.

The next day the entry in the notes read, *"Bizarre – up and dressed independently but wandering aimlessly up and down the ward with bundles of his own clothing."* The word bizarre now featured regularly in the notes, for *"he would do things such as putting toothpaste in his shoe"*. On occasions vestiges of his pleasant self would surface. In a reality orientation group he was *"always polite and sat happily throughout"* and despite his agitated attempts to leave he would do whatever he was asked, so *"you can always get him to return with ease"*. On the sixth day his anti-psychotic medication was increased.

One week after admission, Mr Abrahams' behaviour

took several turns for the worse. His determination to leave the ward escalated. One day he set off the alarm three times and *"each time it was more difficult to persuade him to come back. Haloperidol given as prescribed"*. Agitation now interfered with his willingness to sit and eat his meals. Two days later a nurse wrote, *"Mr Abrahams is unable to perform own personal hygiene... Incontinent of urine x 4 yesterday afternoon... to be encouraged to attend 2 hourly and void urine in toilet."* The next day he *"Dressed inappropriately, wearing two shirts, refused any assistance from nursing staff. Getting verbally abusive when told to take one of his shirts off."* The day after he became very aggressive, hitting and kicking out at staff when they attempted to change his wet clothes. *"Clothes removed to prevent Stanley redressing in day clothes. Mattress removed from bed as patient continually laying down trying to sleep since early afternoon."* He was prescribed the sedative Temazepam to be given at night when necessary.

Mrs Abrahams visited and became upset when she was told about the frequency with which her husband was wetting and soiling himself. She wondered whether her husband's incontinence was the result of the major tranquilliser he was being prescribed. She agreed when told it was not realistic to believe that her husband would return home and so it would be best if she looked for a suitable nursing home.

Mr Abrahams continued to be restless. He would always resist efforts to change his clothes even though they were *"foul, smelling and wet"*. He isolated himself in his room. He would pace the ward and at times briefly sit in the dayroom, but on most occasions he would be found sitting by himself, sometimes in his room, at other times in somebody else's bedroom. Over the next two weeks his behaviour revealed more and more the tragedy that had overtaken him:

- *"Quite resistive this morning when assisted to wash and dress – aggressive and angry with no idea what he should be doing."*
- *"Incontinent of faeces – bathed with much reluctance. Very aggressive when clothes removed."*
- *"Was incontinent of urine. He was very resistive and aggressive when getting ready for bed."*
- *"Reluctant to leave his room. Angry when people approach him."*
- *"Very restless and agitated."*

Mr Abrahams' Haloperidol was increased again. He was now taking six times the original dose.

Flashes of Mr Abrahams' previous self had become increasingly rare. Comments such as *"pleasant and helpful this morning"*, *"smiling and quite communicative this afternoon"* were few and far between. Instead the sense we get from the records is of his inability to survive on the ward, let alone flourish. Perplexing demands, inappropriate expectations, a loss of dignity, an absence of compassion, a failure to 'know him' and a desire to control his behaviour dominated his time in hospital. It was a malignant social world made worse by the use of anti-psychotic medication. Can we imagine how the man who had arrived so elegantly dressed felt being made to walk the ward in his pyjamas? Is it a too great a leap of the imagination to reflect that he may at times have picked on this as a cue to sleep? And what did the ward staff do? They removed the mattress from his bed. The weight chart captures the extent of his physical decline. On the second day of his hospital stay he weighed 83.0kg. When he was discharged he weighed 76.1kg.

He arrived at the nursing home in the company of a nurse escort. I think we can be certain that Mr Abrahams' arrival did not draw the same favourable comments and observations that eloquently communicated the sentiments of all who were touched by his bearing and appearance just five weeks earlier.

Mrs Abrahams was to die 18 months later. She had been suffering from breast cancer but had said little since she had been diagnosed, so all-consuming had been her husband's plight. For the remaining five years of his life Mr Abrahams never knew of his loss. He died in 2000. However, this was not to be the end of his story.

The decision Mr Abrahams had come to nine years earlier was the legacy that now involved me in his story. Weeks after he had been referred to the hospital, and three months before he was diagnosed with Alzheimer's disease, he had changed his will. When the will was read the changes provoked a schism in the family and two relatives took action to have it declared invalid due to "Mr Abraham's lack of testamentary capacity" with the intent that probate be revoked. In other words, they were saying that even though he had yet to be diagnosed with Alzheimer's disease, at the time Mr Abrahams changed his will he was not intellectually competent to do so.

As the progression of dementia is subtle and insidious this was a valid claim to make, but was the disease so advanced to have undermined Mr Abrahams' competence when he changed his will? We know that he had been suffering from memory problems for around three years when his wife first spoke to their family doctor, but was this sufficient to render him incapable of decision-making? In January 2002, 10 years after Mr Abrahams signed his will I was asked to give an opinion.

In the spirit of the seemingly unsure television detective Colombo, rather than the forensically astute Sherlock Holmes, I entered the labyrinthine world of friendships and family relationships.

My starting point was that, even though I knew what was to come, competence at the time a decision is made should be assumed, that incapacity must be demonstrated and that any statement on incapacity must always be specific to the decision under consideration. The decision to change a will does not require an intact memory. It required Mr Abrahams to have the ability to remember for a length of time sufficient to comprehend what was being said or advised, and to be able to demonstrate reasoning and judgement within that period.

The latter is known as 'executive functioning' and embraces the highest intellectual ability that is necessary for appropriate and responsible adult conduct. This is often damaged early in the progression of dementia and so the prospects of upholding Mr Abrahams' legacy did not appear favourable.

Very quickly it became evident that the terms of the revised will were not only consistent with Mr and Mrs

Abrahams' known network of family and friends at the time, they also reflected the actions of those who were closest to and most supportive of them both. This was a good sign. As I talked with family and friends, as well as reviewing the statements of people who knew Mr and Mrs Abrahams, it also became clear that despite his memory failings, throughout 1991 Mr Abrahams appeared able and rational in all that he did. This continued until the summer of 1992. From that time 'odd behaviour' and 'confusion' began to reign. Yet do not the concerns following his fall in the previous autumn, the clinical data gathered at the beginning of 1992 and the diagnosis given in April 1992 argue otherwise? The discrepancy is not that surprising.

Following his fall Mr Abrahams appears to have experienced an acute confusional state that was superimposed on his dementia. This resolved once the traumatic shock abated. From then on, as Alzheimer's disease took hold, Mr Abrahams revealed a progressively worsening dementia – but could the assessment at the beginning of 1992 have exaggerated the extent of his decline?

The assessment involved him attending a strange and probably anxiety-provoking clinical setting well away from the familiarity of everyday routines. In a place he did not know, he was asked challenging questions and had to complete tasks he was unlikely to have ever encountered before. While this 'pure' assessment enabled an accurate diagnosis to be made and for that it is to be commended, the risk that flows from conducting assessments as an 'away rather than a home fixture' is that it can exaggerate weaknesses and fail to acknowledge personal strengths.

The examination employed standard screening tests. While Mr Abrahams scored below the cut-off points for cognitive impairment, analysis of the results revealed that he scored poorly only on the test items that measured memory, orientation and word-finding. Other abilities, such as attention, language comprehension, perception, praxis (the co-ordination of movement) and even abstract thinking were well preserved. These results revealed that Mr Abrahams' dementia was not widespread.

Even within the domains of memory and orientation, how reliable were the results? For example, he had been asked where he was, the name of the place he was in, the day, the date and the year. He had not done well. However, the natural state of affairs is not to remember. We only remember what is personally relevant or significant. In other words, what we might need in the future, which may be very practical or reflect a wish to one day remember a joyous event or a lesson learned. Everything else is responded to and then all but immediately discarded. Not forgotten, but never remembered. Not being able to recall an experience or piece of information later is only evidence of forgetfulness if there has been an initial attempt to remember it.

How essential was it for Mr Abrahams to remember the finer points of orientation? His wife had accompanied him to the hospital. Knowing this, he did not need to remember the name and location of the clinic. In other words, the information was of little functional value. What do we do with information that is not needed? We do not forget it; we make no attempt to remember it in the first place. Similarly, Mr Abrahams lived a lifestyle in

31

which every day was very much the same. Which day it was really did not matter. Are we traumatised when we lose track of the days on holiday? Do we terminate the holiday and seek an urgent memory assessment? It would be strange if we did. Instead it feels like a blessed release from the pressures of everyday responsibilities and obligations. A similar state of affairs applied to Mr Abrahams.

At a time of failing cognitive powers we should expect an able insightful person who is attempting to adapt to their deteriorating memory to do what they have always done, but to an even greater degree: in other words, to retain only that which is truly essential. The assessment should have examined Mr Abrahams' 'meaningful memory' and it had not done so. Because the questions it asked were irrelevant, it was not possible to say that the assessment had established the true severity of his forgetfulness, which I have defined elsewhere as "an inability to retain and recall that which is essential for daily life". (To be able to do so demonstrates 'meaningful memory'). As a consequence it could be argued that the assessment might have underestimated Mr Abrahams' ability to remember what was meaningful and essential. The psychiatrist had accurately diagnosed his dementia – what was open to dispute was the matter of severity.

As Grace showed us in chapter one, a person with psychological reserves such as ingenuity (at the assessment it was estimated that Mr Abrahams' intelligence was in the superior range) can develop ways of adjusting that can lead to constructive ways of living. In early dementia when in familiar places surrounded by cues that support memory, the effects of neurological damage can for periods of time be held at bay, while the preservation of stored autobiographical memories, emotional memory, acquired knowledge, language comprehension, semantic understanding (the knowledge of what words mean) and procedural memory (the memory of skills) all serve to aid adjustment. My opinion was that this is what was happening for Mr Abrahams until the summer of 1992. For periods of time, of increasingly short duration, and when in places he knew, he could give the impression of unimpaired functioning. In particular, his excellent social skills more than likely provided him with a socially adept cloak to wear. It was unsurprising that, aside from his wife, the first person to notice anything was amiss was the gardener with whom Mr Abrahams had daily contact.

The first objective – placing his supposed cognitive frailties in context – had been achieved. The friends and family who described him at this time were not lying for the purposes of monetary gain. At the time of his assessment Mr Abrahams was not as incapacitated as might have been imagined. Even in the months that followed, when in familiar surroundings with people he knew he fared well, for these were the times when he was able to exercise the intellectual resilience necessary to be his normal self.

The next question was key to the matter of competence. Had the examination not only exaggerated the severity of his memory deficit but also failed to assess the critical intellectual ability necessary for altering a will, namely executive functioning? If this was so, then the belief that Mr Abrahams did not possess the mental capacity to change his will just weeks before the assessment commenced would be less tenable.

On balance the examination had not assessed executive functioning because the tests used were not designed to do so. Uncertainty therefore remained. Mr Abrahams' popularity was now to serve him well. He had many friends who were only too happy to share their memories of 'Stan'. They told me of his good humour, his interests in antique furniture and wine, his shrewd insight and, even though more than ten years had elapsed, of an event that occurred on New Year's Day 1992. It was an occasion that the central figure in the story has to this day no recall of at all.

Mr Abrahams and his wife were taking a short holiday. They arranged to have lunch at their hotel with close friends who lived nearby, along with the friends' son and his family. The friends pick up the story: "Stan said we should all meet up. He liked nothing more than what he called a good table. So we did." All gathered for lunch. As the meal unfolded the little girl, who was just two years old, became bored, and unsurprisingly tears started to flow. "Stan left the table to go to the toilet. At least that's what he said. But he actually went up to their room and came back with my granddaughter's Christmas present. Her face was a picture. You see that was Stan: generous and considerate to a fault. He'd said nothing because he hadn't want to spoil Becky's surprise."

This act of kindness revealed much about Mr Abrahams' intellectual abilities, and what is often called emotional intelligence. His response to the little girl's tantrum showed all those higher executive functions required to solve problems. He had displayed empathy and a regard for the feelings of others. He had reasoned a solution, exercised discretion and was then able to put his plan into action by finding his way to his room in an unfamiliar hotel setting, locate the present – and the right one at that – and then return. Why was this event so significant? It had occurred between him visiting his solicitor to change his will and returning to sign the document.

In other words, it happened at the very time I needed to know whether he possessed executive capacity. Mr Abrahams' generosity of spirit and exquisite charm served him well, both during his life and beyond. His legacy had been preserved not so much by my forensic research but by the manner of the man. He had reaped what he had sown, except for a period of 35 days when who he was sadly no longer seemed to matter. Did he ever matter again? Was he rediscovered in the care home? Sadly, I do not know.

&

THREE

The survivor's affair

"You expect me to believe that? If you can't think of anything better to say then tell me nothing. I'm not a fool."

Again Colin had arrived home late. Sometimes from work, at other times from the pub or a jazz club. He would give the lamest of excuses. He had mislaid his car keys, he hadn't been able to find the car, he had left his jacket behind or he had got lost. Colin would plead that he was telling the truth. He could give no reason for his incompetence, but he assured Helen that his irritating and at times embarrassing lapses of memory were genuine. "Are you worrying about something? Are you stressed? Is work getting on top of you?" No, Colin felt fine, maybe a touch tired but who wouldn't be working in publishing? One pressing deadline was always followed by another. He had lived with that for years. "No, there's nothing wrong."

There clearly was and Helen had been there once

before. Her first marriage had been destroyed by her ex-husband's affairs. The signs were the same. Coming in late for no good reason, being unexpectedly delayed, not being so interested in her or the home and those infuriating periods of distracted silence. Because it wasn't just Colin's supposed absent-mindedness that was bothering her. These past few weeks, because weeks are all we are talking about, Colin had seemed different. Nothing much, but little things. He was quieter at times, sometimes seemingly lost in thought. He wasn't as caring. Yes, she had been here before. "Admit it. Who is she? I know you're having an affair." Colin wouldn't argue, he would just protest his innocence and walk off.

This had all come out of the blue. Their marriage was happy. She gave Colin space. Until they had met eight years ago, he had never countenanced marriage. It wasn't that he was simply wrapped up in his career. He also had his circle of friends with whom he shared a passion for jazz. Not only spending hours in clubs listening to what he called his 'mood music', but also on stage playing a smooth and heartfelt saxophone. In turn Helen felt that she was with someone who truly loved her. Colin was gentle and amusing man, who somewhat late in life had found in Helen his 'best friend and soulmate'. And yet now a palpable sense of betrayal was in the air.

Days after a major row, when for the first time Colin had argued back, a work colleague telephoned Helen to tell her that Colin had been crying at work. That night Colin sat in their lounge saying over and over again, "I don't know what's wrong with me." Helen was trying to make sense of it all. Had she been wrong? Was Colin having a breakdown? By the end of that week Helen was worried for her husband. She was noticing all sorts of little things that were not as they ought to be. Colin would not always flush the toilet; he would leave the cap off the toothpaste. And then the clumsiness started. She had always kept Colin away from the dishwasher for he had never grasped the concept of how to load it properly, but this was different. "It was like he was drunk; you know, a bit tipsy." Stumbling as he went up the stairs, reaching out to pick up a glass and knocking it over or letting the front door keys slip through his fingers. Nothing dramatic but all noticeable, uncontrollable and most worryingly happening more and more often.

Colin agreed to see his doctor. An appointment was made for the end of the week. By then the involuntary movements and spasms had started. "I could see that he [the doctor] was worried. He said he had no real idea what was wrong with Colin but he was certain that Colin wasn't having a nervous breakdown." They talked about Colin's moods, his memory problems, his clumsiness and uncontrollable twitches and jerks. "He said that he would make an urgent referral for Colin to see a neurologist."

To this day Helen does not know how she survived the next three weeks. The days could be both comic and awful. Colin would struggle with his words, saying one thing but meaning another; he would walk around with one shoe on and one shoe off; he would try to put sugar in his tea with a fork. Helen was alarmed at how fast Colin was deteriorating. He was not only unable to go to work, but she felt ill at ease leaving him alone for any period of time. It was fortunate that she ran her own public relations company for she was able to schedule her work commitments so she spent most of the time working from home. "It was difficult to know what to do. Colin seemed to be at his best when sitting alone with his music. Playing it low, sort of in the background." And that was another change. Normally Helen would know where Colin was in the house as the sound of music would be all consuming, played at a volume she often found difficult to bear. But now Colin was sensitive. Not to her, but to loud noise and "he was always complaining that the lights were too bright".

The neurologist was matter of fact. Helen recalled him saying that he had conducted a full physical and neurological examination including an EEG, and along with her description of Colin's symptoms he had little doubt that her husband was suffering from a progressive neurological disease known as Creuzfeldt-Jakob disease (CJD), a rare and fatal cause of dementia that in most cases seems to strike at random. He said that nothing could be done. Helen was devastated, but in a strange way not really surprised. She had never heard of CJD but for days she had feared that what was unfolding before her eyes was terrible. However, nothing had prepared her for what the consultant said next. Colin's life expectancy was unlikely to be more than a few months. He explained that nearly three quarters of patients with CJD die within six months of symptoms appearing, some within weeks.

"It was cold and clinical. In many ways it was what I needed to hear. I didn't want false hope or cheery misplaced optimism. I wanted to know what we were going to have to face. But there wasn't going to be a 'we'.

Colin was not only going to die in months, but he would lose insight into his condition very soon. His awareness of what was going on around him would go. One day he would no longer know me. The consultant told me that I must contact social services. He said that Colin would eventually need a nursing home and then, chillingly, as if Colin had already ceased to exist, he said "a man's dying is more the survivor's affair than his own". I later learnt this was a quote from Thomas Mann. I think it was his way of saying take care of yourself, but at the time it didn't help. I left the hospital in a daze. Nothing seemed real. And then Colin stumbled and I was back in the real world of having to cope."

Colin did deteriorate rapidly, but it was not just more of the same. Every day brought a fresh challenge. His sleep was disturbed so, come the morning, Helen often felt exhausted. Colin was more and more clumsy and increasingly unsteady on his feet. He was easily startled, but one morning he was worse and clearly frightened. He kept talking about people breaking in. Nothing Helen said would calm him. When he started stacking furniture up against the front door and shouting for help she feared for his sanity.

In a panic Helen telephoned their GP. He wasn't sure what was best to do but as ever he was understanding and supportive. He contacted a psychiatrist who in turn suggested that he make an urgent referral to the older adult psychiatric team, for they would have access to services and support for people with dementia. For the first time Helen felt she was not just in receipt of a diagnosis. Medication was prescribed to take the edge off Colin's anxiety. A community psychiatric nurse and a social worker started to visit. There was a sense that at times they were struggling to understand what was going on, especially the speed with which Colin was deteriorating, but that didn't matter. What was important was that there were now people to hand whom she could rely on for guidance. Sometimes all she needed to know was that they were there. For weeks she had cursed friends for abandoning them and making her feel so alone. Now she found talking to virtual strangers with whom she shared only a concern for Colin brought tremendous relief. She would talk of her anger, her sadness and her desperate bargaining for a future with Colin. She had once doubted him, but Helen now displayed a warm and genuine attachment. Suspicions and accusations no longer coloured the deep love she felt for her husband. How different from the torment she had felt just a few months earlier.

On any measure of intellectual ability Colin would now do appallingly. He was unable to do anything for himself and Helen needed the support of a homecare worker. They had always tried to involve Colin in his care plan but this was now difficult to do as he was aware of little that was going on around him and his speech was increasingly slurred and indistinct. A case conference was called and it was agreed that the time was approaching when Colin's increasingly complex needs would be best met in a nursing home. This was not because services had failed him, but as Colin's journey had rapidly progressed ever closer to him requiring continuous observation and care, having to look after him for what seemed to be every waking moment had started to overwhelm Helen.

Three weeks later he was admitted to a nursing home registered for dementia care. It was here that I met Helen and Colin for the first time.

I had been asked to advise the home as none of the nurses had experience caring for a person with CJD. Fears and myths abounded, made worse by occasional sensationalised articles in the media. Is CJD infectious? If so, isn't it transmitted through blood? Would he have to be barrier nursed (nursed in isolation with strict hygiene rules)? My own experience was limited. I had worked with two people with probable CJD, one of whom had his diagnosis confirmed by post-mortem. The other person died just five days after being admitted to a care home and I never learned the outcome of her post-mortem.

I talked with the care team and helped them gain a sense of perspective. Their greatest concern was infection control. They were assured that compliance with standard infection control procedures would be sufficient to manage any clinical risk. In many ways the message was 'ensure you do what you would be expected to do'. So the necessity to prevent skin breakdown was emphasised. The sole precautionary measure was to keep blood work to a minimum. Information from the Alzheimer's Society's CJD support network was shared with the staff team to alleviate their anxieties. Of great importance was introducing a care plan that was responsive to Colin's advancing dependency needs but which did not result in meaningless care actions and medical interventions that would work against providing Colin with the best possible quality of life and ultimately a comfortable and dignified death.

In his final weeks of life, the vision we strove to share was one of Colin as a person, as opposed to him being seen as the remnant of a horrific neurological disease, for in truth Colin was beyond deficits. We needed to respond to that which remained and not pay too much heed to that which had been lost. Yes, there was a need for skilled nursing and agreed care protocols, but Colin as a person would be to the forefront of our thinking throughout. In this we were helped by Helen who clearly needed the time and opportunity to talk about the man who had meant the world to her.

Somehow she got herself into work every day but sooner rather than later she would be heading to the nursing home, often arriving by lunchtime. Sometimes you could see she was suffering the deepest grief and darkness. On a particularly bad day she sobbed uncontrollably. That morning she had forgotten how it felt to kiss Colin goodbye before leaving for work. Standing by the front door she could not even picture his face. Distraught – and as she said, "it was crazy. Irrational, but I had to do it" – she raced around the house rearranging pictures of Colin and their moments together, even putting out photographs that had been in drawers for years. "I feel so guilty," she exclaimed. "I'm crying for me, not for Colin." Thomas Mann's words began to ring true.

Over the few weeks that followed, Colin's physical deterioration was rapid. His problems with balance and co-ordination – known as cerebellar ataxia - made eating, drinking, standing and walking difficult. His sudden and involuntary jerking movements and grimaces were distressing to see. Helen believed that it was because his deterioration was in the beginning inexplicable and then ultimately frightening to witness that friends had rarely visited. Even phone calls had been few and far between. Nobody, not even Helen, knew what to say.

To avoid overstimulation the curtains in Colin's room were always partially drawn with a table lamp throwing out a soft light across the room. The nurses were reminded of the value of creating a quiet and calm environment. When caring for Colin's physical needs they were gentle, kept sudden movements to a minimum and even though Colin could probably no longer comprehend they introduced themselves and softly talked to him about what they intended to do. Medication was used to control his involuntary muscle movements and grimacing, but often with little obvious benefit.

"Would his 'mood music' help?" enquired Helen. He loved music. He always had. "Colin always said it helped him unwind." I was sceptical, but we had nothing to lose. So we recruited David Sanborne, Kenny G, Courtney Pine, Dave Brubeck and others onto the care team. The room was a delight. The music Colin liked so much now provided a soothing and familiar backdrop to the nursing interventions that characterised Colin's days. The transformation, although by no means total, was both marvellous and a relief to see. For lengthy periods of time Colin was calm. Even on his most disturbed days his clumsy and ill-coordinated movements would in moments be less obvious and Helen was certain there was the occasional trace of a smile. Helen would say, "It is so him." Now and again even a few of his friends dropped into "Colin's place." How real was the change in Colin?

I am not sure. Were we seeing changes in how others felt? Definitely. Whatever was happening, the care plan resonated with a new rhythm. And Helen was coping better than she had for weeks.

However, the degeneration remained unceasing. Soon Colin was unable to move or speak, and swallowing became difficult. Motionless and mute (known as akinetic mutism), Colin was unaware of what was going on around him, even though at times his eyes would appear to follow you. And still the music played.

There was nothing to be gained by stopping it, and who knows – at some level of consciousness those soulful sounds might still have been making a connection. One of the care team, sometimes me, would always try to make ourselves available to Helen, for as Colin slowly moved toward death I knew at times she felt terribly alone with her thoughts and memories.

Colin died on a Wednesday. Helen had been with him continuously for nearly 30 hours. She was devastated but conducted herself with great dignity. We spoke later that day but then as is so often the way circumstances conspired against us and it will always be a matter of regret for me that I never saw her again. Even though she had been stricken by a terrible loss in a manner that was unimaginably tragic, my hope has always been that as the years have passed she is doing more than just surviving.

&

FOUR

A man no longer known

AR Luria wrote "A man does not consist of memory alone" but Mr Bryan was to find out that life without memory is no life at all. Without it he felt he was nothing. Denied respect, facing embarrassment, fearing ridicule, he coped in ways that felt right for him. In the process he destroyed his marriage.

I was asked to see Mr Bryan by his GP. He had become increasingly forgetful and temperamental, and his wife could no longer cope. I visited him at his home and we spoke at length. Our conversation lasted for nearly half an hour and therein lay the issue. We had held a meaningful conversation that was not bedevilled by errors and incomprehensible utterances. On a few occasions he had repeated himself, and twice, without noticing, he selected the wrong word. The signs suggested early Alzheimer's disease. Yet the severity of his dementia was minimal. Not only had he conversed well, I was sitting opposite a man who was smart, shaven and well groomed, and

I knew he had done this all himself. So why could his wife not cope?

Out of the corner of my eye as I spoke with Mr Bryan I could see his wife in the kitchen, quietly seething. I spoke with her and explained that it was too soon to say what was wrong with her husband and our assessment would have to continue. However, from what I had just seen and heard he had come over as able and, while not a man you could easily warm to, quite amiable. So why was life with him so difficult? Mrs Bryan went on to tell me that her husband had always been critical and opinionated. He had never suffered fools gladly, nor could he tolerate weaknesses in himself. Such intolerance was now not helping him adjust to his failing memory. She would tell him, "Stop trying to remember messages when people call: write them down." He wouldn't do it, for that was an admission of weakness. She would say, "Stop fretting about what you have to do, have a diary for the day, and then you'll know what you have done and what still needs to be done." He wouldn't do that either, for again it would be evidence of weakness. This infuriated her.

Mrs Bryan was a retired schoolteacher. She knew best. She also had standards. Mrs Bryan began to relate to her husband less as a wife, and more as a parent. This was not a deliberate thought-out intention, but as her husband became less competent we began to observe what leading dementia authority Tom Kitwood called 'infantilization'. Rather than seeing her husband as a man with ways and needs increasingly similar to those of a child, she saw him as having become a child.

As the months passed Mrs Bryan became less and less

tolerant of her husband. Within moments of coming together she would tell him about something he should have done differently or better, or something he might have forgotten to do. Their relationship had deteriorated so badly that when she walked into a room he would walk out. He no longer waited for the criticism. Eventually he was driven to be not only apart from his wife, but to be outside in the garden. Within minutes of getting himself ready for the day he would be outside. I talked to him and it became clear that his reasons were complex, but also unsurprising. His desire was not just to be away from his wife. Pointing to the window he said, "Out there I don't fail. It's physical not mental. Maybe my memory is not as good as it was, but I'm 67, what can you expect? But out there it's different." To assuage his fears Mr Bryan was sheltering behind the myth that ageing brings with it profound memory impairment destined to usher in dependency and disorientation. In response he sought new endeavours to sustain and replenish his self-esteem.

But 'out there' he was still making mistakes. As it became increasingly difficult for him to remember what he had and hadn't done and his reasoning became more and more suspect, he would weed, prune, cut the grass, trim the hedges and turn the soil several times each day. While his errors and misjudgements were not readily apparent to him, of greater importance was that his wife was not close by telling him what he was doing wrong. He now had peace of mind, unknowingly at a price.

Mrs Bryan did not see a solution, and did not feel comforted by her husband's actions. She felt the loss of their relationship and the loneliness. Lonely, not simply because there was so little time with her husband, but also because friends had stopped visiting and neighbours no longer called round.

Mr Bryan didn't like people coming to their home. He had always been a reserved, private man, but now he would say, "No more. I don't want people here. I make a fool of myself. I forget names, I don't recognise people, I lose the thread of the conversation." He went on, "And never again do I want to see that expression on people's faces that immediately tells me that I have repeated myself. They can never hide it." So if people called round, without saying anything he would get up and walk out. On most occasions he would already be outside. His wife would beckon him in, and he would stare right through her and carry on with what he was doing. Everybody felt awkward, so people stopped calling. They would say, "George doesn't want us here. We understand. It can't be easy for him, but we would still love to see you. Come round anytime. We could go out for the day." And how Mrs Bryan would have loved to, but she couldn't.

She would say to me, "I am so bored and lonely. You can't know how much I want to see my friends, but how can I? He still does stupid things. He won't listen. I could go out and he'll decide to cook himself something to eat. I'll come back and who knows what he might have done to the kitchen. He might even set the house on fire. You see, I can't."

Not only was Mrs Bryan lonely, she was isolated and increasingly saw herself as being trapped. However, rather than confiding that she was struggling with a caring role she had never wanted – for as she was to tell me later, "guilt comes easily to me, and I do it well" – she decided to manipulate events.

The Bryans were a reasonably affluent couple. Mr Bryan had risen to be a senior executive working for a large manufacturing company. They lived in an attractive semi-detached house on an open plan estate. One day, Mrs Bryan decided to leave the side gate open. She knew what she was doing. It now meant her husband had free access to the front garden. As time passed he was just as likely to take the wheelbarrow, lawnmower and his garden tools out there and start work, as he was to stay in the rear garden. Unfortunately, when out front Mr Bryan did not always appreciate where his garden ended and his neighbours' gardens started. Tolerance soon evaporated. Trespass and damage soon led to frayed tempers and confrontations. Prized shrubs were rendered barren stumps, flowerbeds were decimated as Mr Bryan, within the limits of his dementia, pruned, planted and generally busied himself in 'his' garden.

Even though Mrs Bryan had engineered it all she struggled to cope. Sitting opposite her GP she broke down, saying her husband's behaviour was impossible. Rightly reluctant to prescribe a major tranquilliser to manage Mr Bryan's challenging behaviours, he assured her that social services would be able to help. He explained that sedation was associated with unwanted side-effects and possible health risks, and only when other measures have been found to be ineffective should sedative medication be tried. A referral to social services would be best.

Two weeks later Mr and Mrs Bryan were visited by a

social worker. She was faced with an articulate, yet exhausted caring wife. Stressed and at the end of her tether, Mrs Bryan described confrontations with neighbours, the reasons for which she could readily understand, for her husband had caused so much damage to their once immaculately manicured gardens. Then there was the road. Her husband had seemingly lost any sense of danger. Yes, it was a quiet suburban road: "But that doesn't mean an accident can't happen. Look at the parked cars," she would often say, "he walks straight out between them. One day he'll cause an accident and somebody will get killed."

Stress, trespass, damage and destruction, let alone the risk of assault and accident all conspired in the mind of the social worker for her to advise that Mr Bryan be admitted to a care home. So, sooner than might have been anticipated, less than three years after my initial visit, Mr Bryan entered a care home to live alongside 15 people with dementia. Not other people with dementia, for in the absence of insight the social grouping of dementia care is not an aggregate of those who know the reality of their lives. For Mr Bryan, his experience was now to be that of living alongside people with whom he had nothing in common.

For us it is so straightforward. If we look into a room and see ten people with dementia, that's exactly what we see. However, if you are one of those ten, you see yourself as you have always been, along with nine... what? Others acting in ways that are not only strange and upsetting, but inexplicable.

As we saw in the story of Mr Abrahams Tom Kitwood wrote about what he called a "malignant social psychology", a term that describes the bleakness of care settings where a person with dementia is no longer treated as a real person, but is instead disempowered, disparaged and has their feelings ignored. While this concept is used to describe the inadequacy of actions taken in the course of care, malignancy is also to be found in the social grouping of dementia. Sitting in a lounge, a person with dementia can be distressed and devalued by the behaviour of those alongside whom they live, as well as by the actions of those who are providing their care.

Mr Bryan was to be in the home for five days. The first four were all the same. Agitated, he would engage with no one. He would spend his time pacing the corridors. On reaching an external door he would start pulling the handle, but all were locked or baffled (some doors on dementia care units and wards are not actually locked but are controlled by digital codes, handles that need to be pulled simultaneously in opposite directions or a discreet supplementary handle. All of these 'baffles' are designed to prevent a person with dementia from leaving). For Mr Bryan there was no sense of arrival. Instead, he felt his confinement. Frustrated, he would angrily bang on the door. If approached he would stare, say nothing and walk away. Eventually he would surface in the lounge. Acknowledging no one he would walk across the room into the conservatory. However, as it was unsafe for residents to be outside unsupervised, the French windows that opened onto the garden were always locked. He would try in vain to open them. Failing, he would start to bang on the glass. As he was now a danger to himself a carer would immediately go over and lead him away.

Saying nothing he would leave the lounge and continue to pace the building. This was his life in the care home.

On the fifth day, the morning unfolded as always. Pacing the corridors, trying door handles, ignoring everyone, he soon found himself in the conservatory. As usual he would start to bang on the glass. Increasingly angry, his pounding became louder. For his own safety one of the care staff rushed over to lead him away. Telling him to calm down she sat him in an armchair in the lounge. Within moments she had walked off as she had 'things to do'. Within seconds Mr Bryan got up from the chair and started to leave the lounge.

The housekeepers were around mopping and buffing the floors. Within a few strides Mr Bryan reached a hazard cone warning of slippery floors. He stopped, picked up the cone, turned and lashed out at a frail dementing woman who was dozing in an armchair by the door. The ferocity was real, the injury horrific.

Immediately Mr Bryan was escorted to the office, and the GP and paramedics called. Mr Bryan's GP requested an immediate admission to hospital. A community psychiatric nurse arrived and accompanied Mr Bryan to the acute psychiatric unit. I was telephoned and given a sketchy outline of what had happened, and was told he had been admitted to the assessment ward. I arrived at the ward 20 minutes later, by coincidence at the very time his wife arrived. Her first words to me were spoken with absolute certainty: "My husband hasn't done this. God, we know he's not an easy man, but he was a gentleman. He never would have raised his hands to a woman. No, my husband's not done this."

Clearly her husband had done it, but when working with people who challenge us, so often we hear families say "that is not my partner/parent", etc. The changed behaviour is taken as testimony to the fact that their loved one has disappeared. To be replaced by who or what? A shell, or maybe a body that is merely seen as the host to a cluster of signs and symptoms of disease. And unfortunately too many practitioners nourish this belief, for whenever a family carer asks why it is that their mother, father, husband or wife screams, wanders away, resists care, or any of the other myriad of actions we struggle to understand, the response is so often simply "it's because they have dementia". Yet if this were so, would not most people with dementia act in the same challenging ways? They share the same pathology, and these are said to be symptoms of that. But we know this is not the whole picture.

People with dementia are different from each other. Move away from the cognitive disability, and what impresses us most is their uniqueness, not their similarity. So why do we degrade their behaviour to symptoms of a disease, rather than seeing it as evidence of efforts to survive in a world that resonates with fear, threat and mystery? Could it be that we no longer see them as people whose feelings need to be acknowledged and their opinions valued? Are we seduced by the simplicity and authority of the disease-model that not only fails to talk of people, but also absolves us of all responsibility? Can we really say that whatever a person with dementia does, it is because they have dementia?

So, were we faced with a meaningless, random act symptomatic of probable Alzheimer's disease, or was his violent assault resonating with a meaning that was consistent with the man once known to us all?

How had Mr Bryan coped with his dementia? By avoiding people and isolating himself in the garden where he would work for hours without break. It was these actions that had initially undermined his wife's capacity to care. Once admitted to a nursing home he had to endure the presence of people every waking moment. It did not matter there was little conversation to avoid, or that the absence of self-awareness meant that his failings were no longer known to him. This once private man simply found people intimidating. He was driven to leave their presence. Yet this does not entirely explain his need to leave the home. There was also a positive pull. For nearly three years he had enjoyed being in the garden. Here he had found peace of mind. Now tempted by the garden, he was unable to reach it. That fateful day, when his frustration knew no bounds, he struck out with tragic effect.

Given our understanding of Mr Bryan and his situation, was the proprietor held to account for confining not only him, but 15 other people within four walls, tempting them with the outside but rarely allowing them the pleasures of reaching the garden? No. The home was seen as providing sensible risk management. You cannot have people with dementia roaming around outside, unaccompanied and unseen in unsafe areas. Who knows what might happen? Undeniably the home provided a safe environment, but did it have to be so restrictive, and can it be said to have offered Mr Bryan a lifestyle he would have wished for?

What degree of responsibility should be ascribed to the social worker? What guidance had she offered Mrs Bryan when looking for an appropriate care home? The home was comfortable, picturesque and nestled in a pleasant setting, but could it ever have met Mr Bryan's needs for privacy and occupation? Or was it the case that his needs had never truly been considered? The documentation provided by the social worker was little more than a litany of problems and complaints. It talked of him "wandering outside" and the destruction he caused, the confrontations and arguments, the hazards and risk of accident and assault, and how his wife could no longer cope with the stress. But what about him? As I turned the pages I wondered when Mr Bryan's story would start. How this proud and reserved man had struggled to accept his failing powers. How he eventually coped by isolating himself from others and ultimately found sanctuary in his garden.

The story never did start. Lip service only had been paid to the meeting of his needs. Was the social worker asked to justify her actions? No. The authority, simplicity and reassurance of the disease model offers us all the opportunity to seek sanctuary in a culture where we never have to question, or be questioned about our own practice. When faced with people with dementia who act in challenging ways we know where responsibility lies – it's because they have dementia!

The reality is that Mr Bryan had presented all who had responsibility for his care with needs to be met, not problems to be managed or symptoms to be contained, and he had been sorely failed. As no care home was prepared to accept him he languished for two years on a hospital ward. It did not matter that his behaviour was now explained in terms of unmet need, the risks were deemed to be too great. Only when frailty overcame him and he was no longer seen as a threat to others was he discharged to a nursing home for people with high dependency needs. He died seven weeks later. His fate was tragic, but it was not his alone. It was shared also by a woman who had been innocently dozing in an armchair.

&

FIVE

Something about his smile

Eight years have passed since I first met John in the conservatory of his neat and tidy home, but I remember that first encounter as if it were yesterday.

A ruddy, cheery face greeted me. Standing erect, bathed in sunshine, he looked a picture of health. His wife introduced me, and as he grasped my hand in a firm handshake, out came a jumbled stream of words, some appropriate, others fragmented. Words jostled for space alongside meaningless neologisms and sounds, most of which I could not understand. Despondency masked his face and he turned away. I heard him say, "its none not no... as if...", then silence. He looked a beaten man. Barbara took me to one side and tearfully told me that her husband's speech was becoming less and less intelligible with each passing month.

Barbara offered to make us all a coffee, I think more to give her the opportunity to compose herself than to be on this occasion the attentive hostess. She retreated into the kitchen. I sat down next to John and as I turned toward him, despondency had been replaced by something I would become so familiar with – a smile so broad it would light up his face.

I soon learned that John loved the company of people. He had many friends. He was actively involved with his local church. Never loud or brash, he was simply a warm and friendly, gentle man. But why smile now, why no despair?

The answer was simple. Even though only minutes had passed he had forgotten that he had struggled to greet me. Forgotten? Yes, but only to a degree. Some self-awareness remained, for during the rest of my time with him that morning he would smile, nod in agreement, but say little. It was evident that he understood far more than he could express. As such he still enjoyed the company of others, even though he could contribute little to the conversation.

Barbara took responsibility for all that went on in the home. Still only 57 years old, John had not worked for five months. While John had yet to be given a formal diagnosis, Barbara knew what was happening. She had seen it before. Her mother had died with Alzheimer's disease earlier that year. As John dramatically deteriorated, everything that had been troubling her for years now made sense.

Although not known at the time, John's story really started four years earlier. He had not been happy at work for what seemed ages, but probably it was no more than months. Nobody knew why. He had worked in the same job for 27 years, so why be so stressed and unhappy now? John either didn't know, or he wouldn't say. His

GP diagnosed work-related stress and depression. John would be signed off sick for a few weeks and then he would return to work. A month or so later he would be off sick again. When at home, aside from being at times unnaturally quiet and distracted, he was his normal self.

One day he came home from work and told his family, "I've handed my notice in." I think all were relieved, for they had known how unhappy he had been. Only three weeks later the family were having dinner together when John announced he had found himself another job. As one the family were delighted. His daughter told me, "Dad hadn't been happy, but having got himself out of that place, he had pulled himself together. He was my Dad again."

"Where are you going to be working?" "It couldn't be better," he replied, "I've got a job in the factory opposite my old place. I'm going to be their caretaker." Ostensibly this meant he would have responsibility for sweeping up between the machinery and the workbenches, and then disposing of the wood shavings. "You can't," they exclaimed. "You're a skilled man. You're a machine operator. You can't." But John stood firm. His mind was made up.

For three years John worked at the factory. As ever he was popular, but soon his new work colleagues realised how prone he was to do the most stupid of things. They all got on well, however, so tolerance and not criticism was the name of the game. They would cover up for him and give him a helping hand. At times he would be the butt of their jokes. They could not resist, but they knew John would take it in good grace. He simply came over as being not the brightest of men. He would sweep the same area over and over again, he would let shavings pile up and seem not to notice, at other times he would forget what he had promised to do or he wouldn't know what to do with the shavings. One day there was a fire alarm practice at the factory. Everyone gathered in the car park but John was nowhere to be found. He was eventually discovered roaming around the factory lost and bewildered. He had not remembered what to do when the alarm sounded and couldn't work out a sensible course of action. There was no way he could continue to be employed in the factory. Health and Safety regulations would not allow it. At this point his employer suggested John go on long-term sick leave while he underwent investigations. Everybody knew John would not be returning.

This was why I was sitting next to John. I had been asked by his GP to "assess and advise". She no longer thought stress and depression were the cause of his deteriorated abilities. With his profile of progressively worsening memory, speech and reasoning a diagnosis of probable Alzheimer's disease was now straightforward to reach – not so easy four years ago. What John had not understood at the time, or possibly been unable to admit, was that his worries at work were because he was concentrating less and less well thanks to Alzheimer's disease. As a result he struggled to grasp the complexity of the machinery and the sequence of the tasks to be done. His mood deteriorated as he felt more and more helpless and frustrated. However, at this most critical point in his life, John demonstrated a strength of spirit that sustained him for three more years. Years in which

61

he preserved his peace of mind and lived a life of treasured normality. By changing jobs he had down-skilled, but he was able to set off to work each day knowing that what was expected of him was within the limits of what he could do. He had not demeaned himself. He had acted with common sense and adjusted to the insidious destruction of his powers.

However, I doubt whether John ever truly knew what he was coping with. Like many people experiencing the beginnings of dementia, John entered a world of dark secrets. I suspect he did all he could to avoid having his fears confirmed or being seen as foolish. In the early times of dementia denial, confabulation (making up stories), being self-centred, blaming others and avoidance are all part of the repertoire. Words are used and actions taken which wrongly give the impression that personality is changing. Behaviour changes, but personality does not. We need to understand that a person is coping with a psychological trauma the magnitude of which we can hardly imagine. Some people cope poorly, others display remarkable resilience for we are all resourced differently. If we take the time to delve beneath a surface that abounds with puzzling and exasperating sights and sounds, we often realise that what was once seen as inexplicable can now be appreciated as resonating with rational intent and common sense.

Who hasn't woken up, maybe when staying away, and for a second or two not known where they were? Within moments the penny drops and we know where we are. But imagine if the penny didn't drop. Despite all our efforts no answer is forthcoming. How would you feel?

Frightened? Would panic start to well up? Those feelings would at least be unfolding in the comfort and security of a bedroom. In dementia not knowing where you are, where you've come from, how you got there and what you are going to do next happens anywhere, at any time. When alone, with others, in the street, in a shop, in a car, on a bus, and it doesn't matter how hard you concentrate, how desperately you search for an answer, the answer rarely comes.

Would you want to go out in those circumstances? If the answer is no, do we have evidence that your personality has altered, or do you remain who you have always been, and it is simply your behaviour that has changed? You are coping with a degree of fear and worry the like of which you have never previously encountered. However, in the process of acting so very differently can it be said that you are acting anything other than sensibly, even if your behaviour baffles all others? And it will baffle them, especially if you choose never to share the reason for your unwillingness to leave home.

John's ability to cope and get on with life had originally muddied the diagnostic waters, but no longer. Barbara gave up her part-time job to care for her husband. As time passed he became more dependent, yet for two years all progressed without a hitch. He attended his local church, friends continued to visit and he would take his dog for a walk. Barbara was unfailingly supportive, often shielding him. I would visit every month to meet them, and while John had great difficulty expressing himself, he would sit in on the conversations and you could tell he still understood more than his speech revealed. He would sometimes manage a few words, at times he would look quizzical, but there was always his smile – it was never to desert him.

After many months of caring without complaint Barbara sensed something sinister was happening. John had always been cheerful, pleasant and co-operative. Now his mood was darker. He was less accepting and at times resistive. What she could not fully appreciate was that nearly six years on, John's dementia was becoming progressively severe. He was now showing signs of agnosia and apraxia (losses of perception and co-ordination). These are not merely neurological losses and dysfunctions to be understood in terms of dependency and care needs. As important is the emotional reaction to these debilitating, frustrating and frightening changes, an inner world of new feelings, chaotic and on occasions extreme. To the detriment of all involved, it is a world too often neglected by professionals.

In the bathroom, John struggled to co-ordinate his movements. He could not easily grasp and pick up his flannel, razor or whatever else he might need. As always Barbara was there to help him. But John was unable to understand why he could not do what he had always done automatically, without conscious thought. He would not have known a time when he could not pick up and appropriately hold whatever he wished for these are basic skills, the origins of which are to be found in the early months of life. This is a time of 'pre-memorial experience' when the brain is immature and does not allow for the recall of what is learnt or done. What is acquired is stored in ancient recesses of our brain as 'implicit memory'. It is what we know of ourselves and which may not require conscious thought. If we drop what we need, we pick it up. If we want something, we reach out and grasp it. Yet John no longer could, and he had no explanation, for he could not seek refuge in the sanctuary of knowing it was because he had dementia. His insight and self-awareness had long since dissolved.

Can we imagine his bewilderment and frustration as he endured an 'internal environment' that he was in no way able to understand? If people are frustrated they become bad-tempered and angry. It is therefore unsurprising that apraxia is associated with aggression. The relationship is not the result of brain tissue degenerating: it is born of frustration. It was John's frustration-related anger that Barbara now had to adjust to, but she did not find this easy for he had always been such a caring and easy-going man. John was also struggling with problems of perception and recognition. Sometimes when given his razor or flannel he would gaze at himself in the mirror and then slowly reach out toward it. Such incidents multiplied, generating perplexity, fear and, on rare occasions, causing John to smile in his self-deprecating way as he appreciated his ludicrous mistake. Realising the 'wrongness' of his actions he would sometimes slowly guide his hand back to his face; at other times he would throw his razor or flannel down in exasperation.

For John's son, a sense that there was "something seriously the matter" occurred when he and his wife took his parents out for a meal. John and his son went to the lavatory. They stood next to each other at the urinals. His son walked over to wash his hands and it must have occurred to him, "Where's Dad?" He turned to see that his father had gone from his urinal to the one that his son had used and was 'washing' his hands in his son's stale urine. Yet he clearly knew that he was doing something wrong for he was gently sobbing. John had wanted to wash his hands. He needed a sink. What he had found was certainly white, and it was made of porcelain. To John he had found a wash basin.

To be agnosic is to see without true knowledge. John scanned his world, he saw – and yet what was he seeing? From what is known of agnosia it is likely that he was picking up on individual features and no longer seeing faces or objects as a whole. A striking brightness, a colour, a shape would arrest his attention. Failing to see the whole, seeing only details, John would misinterpret, sometimes because he would fill in the gaps with non-existent features.

Summer turned into autumn. Days once bright and sun-filled were now dismal and overcast. With clocks turned back, dusk came ever earlier. Nights drew in and for John life took a terrifying turn. He would see his reflection in the television screen, catch a glimpse of himself in the windows, but to John these were other people. He would get out of his chair, point, wave his arms, glare and shout, "Go, gone away!" But if you shout at your reflection what does it do – it shouts back. He would race over to the windows and, still shouting, bang on the glass. Barbara was alarmed by her husband's behaviour. "There's nobody there," she would say. She would comfort him by telling him there was nothing for him to worry about. Yet John could not be consoled. He couldn't believe Barbara because in his world he knew there was something wrong. Torment and fear characterised his daily life. Barbara tried to remain compassionate but his outbursts were wearing her down. One day John was standing in the conservatory and he became extremely agitated. As Barbara was guiding him away from the window it is said that John lashed out to hit her. My belief is that he had not. I think he was trying to get her behind him, an action fuelled not by a wish to harm but motivated by a need to protect her from the people he was seeing. Despite appearances to the contrary, John remained her devoted husband. The problem was that Barbara was less and less able to see it this way.

It is an 'overlearned' behaviour from childhood that toilets are usually upstairs. When John needed the toilet, up he would go. Having reached the landing, apraxia and agnosia were unforgiving companions. He was rarely able to toilet successfully. He would have problems with his clothing: belts, buckles, button and zips were insurmountable obstacles. He would wet himself; or if he had been able to adjust his clothing he would urinate on the floor, up the wall or in the bath. But John could not appreciate how dependent he had become for he had fallen prey to what happens to all people with dementia. When John had known he needed Barbara, he had needed her least, but when he needed her most John didn't know it at all.

Unlike John, Barbara knew the difficulties he would face. She would follow him upstairs and be met with hostility. He was frustrated. He could not think why this person (for I believe on many occasions John did not recognise his wife now) was interfering with his need for privacy during this most personal act. Barbara was at breaking point. She would say, "Why is he doing this to me?" "What's happened to the man I married?"

At about five o'clock one morning Barbara crossed her personal Rubicon. She was woken by John. He was standing in front of the dressing table urinating into the top drawer. She threw herself out of bed and rushed over to him. She wasn't thinking clearly. "I wanted to get him away. Into the toilet, I don't know. I just wanted it to be over. No... I mean... I wanted him to stop." It was barely light. She was coming in from behind. As she grabbed him, John was caught unawares. I doubt whether it does justice to how John felt at this moment to say he was startled. He spun round and hit her. Barbara, momentarily stunned, looking into eyes that gave no hint of recognition, slapped his face. Is it any wonder that four hours later she telephoned the community psychiatric nurse saying she could no longer cope?

Within 72 hours John was in respite care. He was scheduled to stay for a week. It was to last less than two days. There were too many windows. He would pace the corridors, raging and banging on the glass. He refused to eat, would push staff away and would often be found agitatedly trying to open the baffle-locked front door. On the Sunday evening the home manager telephoned Barbara to say they could not cope with John's behaviour and could she collect him the next morning. Barbara duly did and found herself in an awful place known as 'guilt'. She knew the quality of care she was able to give to a man who she no longer felt to be her husband was sorely lacking in patience and compassion, yet she now also knew how tormented he would be living in a care home. Whichever way she turned she knew that she and John would both suffer.

As we talked it was clear that now was the time to give Barbara permission to let go. She could take no more. No more talking about how John was still the same caring gentle man with whom she had shared the past thirty-something years. We had talked at length about how his changed manner and behaviour were not signs of disease but evidence of how he had become a frightened and tormented man trying to survive in a world we can hardly comprehend. Now the time was right for her to move on and end the anguish that comes with knowing that a loved one is suffering. He appeared a stranger. Was it not possible that he had been eaten away by the illness; leaving behind a shell, recognisable as John but no longer John, the man she had known and loved for years? Within three months of allowing Barbara to speak of symptoms, John entered a nursing home. It was a home not with a reputation for 'managing difficult behaviour', but one where carers look beyond what a person does into their subjective world of motivation and feelings.

With their understanding of John's psychology and a true commitment to his emotional needs, his adjustment has been pleasing to see for he lives in relative tranquillity. His problems with co-ordination and recognition are accommodated within a care plan that is designed to meet his need for peace of mind, not to control his aggressive outbursts. Personal care is characterised by approaches that are gentle and tolerant, and are not affected by the demands of time-limited routines. He spends much of his time in either his bedroom or a small lounge. In both rooms there are neither mirrors nor televisions, and in the evening the curtains are always closed. In the absence of reflection 'strangers' no longer torment him. John will sit quietly for long periods. Whenever possible a nurse will spend time with him. There is no conversation but that does not matter. Being in the company of a person with untroubled eyes and a reassuring smile does just fine. When his wife visits some sense of familiarity is observed for that smile is never slow to appear. On occasions John sparkles in her company. Barbara asks for nothing more, for she also has now found peace of mind.

&

SIX

"That's not our aunt!"

Janet was a woman in her late fifties. Somewhat old-fashioned in her ways, she lived with her 93-year-old mother. It had always been so, for Janet had never left home. The youngest of five, she had seen her brothers and sisters leave the nest. They hadn't gone far, probably because theirs was a close knit family. Even the two who went away to college returned. One by one they married, set up their own homes and as time passed had children of their own. Janet never did. She was content to live at home with her parents, and after her father died, happy for it to be just the two of them, mother and daughter, living quietly together. Their togetherness was never borne out of necessity. Janet's mother was a delightful woman, bright and more alive than many women 20 years her junior. Janet was simply set in her familiar ways and happy to be her mother's companion.

This is not to suggest that Janet had allowed life to pass her by. She was respected and held in great affection by many in her neighbourhood. For nearly 30 years she had been the manager of the kitchen and dining room of the local primary school. Generations of small children had grown up knowing of Janet's tender and caring ways. She was described by many as simply being a very nice woman. Always considerate, never having a bad word to say about anyone, she would put herself out even for those she hardly knew. Nobody could recall her ever raising her voice, let alone falling out with people. To her nieces and nephews she was their favourite aunt, warm and welcoming, always happy to see them.

Janet was 59 years old when her mother unexpectedly died. Without drama or crisis she passed away in her sleep. For the first time Janet was on her own. She sold the small family house, and bought a maisonette a short walk from the school, just two streets away from where one of her brothers and his family lived. She worked for one more year and then retired. I think it can be said that she enjoyed the next four years. She took full advantage of the time she now had to be with her family, devoting herself not only to her nieces and nephews, but to their young children as well. But change was afoot.

When asked about the beginnings of a loved one's dementia, many families do not speak about a specific incident that alarmed them. Instead there is a slow realisation, a mounting sense that something is not right. For Janet's family it was her shabbiness. Janet began to wear the same clothes day after day, either not noticing or caring that her blouse, jumper, skirt were grubby and stained. Embarrassingly there was also a body odour. Perplexed and feeling awkward, her family said nothing, but one day a sister asked what was wrong. The reply was troubling. Janet denied there was anything the matter, but it was not what she said that so concerned her sister, it was how she said it. She bit her sister's head off. The word went round the family: "Don't go there." Months passed and their concerns deepened. They shared a sense that something awful was happening to their sister. It was no longer just her appearance that was unkempt: Janet's home was heading the same way. Untidy, unclean, the kitchen in particular was often in a sorry state, with crockery and cutlery lying around unwashed for days on end. Again Janet seemed either oblivious to all that was happening, or she didn't care. Nothing was said.

Then the telephone calls started. She would ring her brothers, sisters, nieces and nephews several times a day, yet it seemed from her conversation that for Janet she had not spoken to them for days, even though it might have been just a few hours ago. Events culminated when Janet got lost returning home from the city centre, a journey she had done hundreds of time. She became so bewildered and distressed she was brought home by the police.

Enough was enough. One of Janet's sisters telephoned her GP and explained all that had been happening and how concerned they all were. Janet's doctor was particularly unhelpful. He appreciated their worries but he said there was nothing he could do. Janet was his patient. He would gladly see her if she visited the surgery, he was even happy to talk to her over the telephone, but until she got in touch his hands were tied. But Janet saw no reason why she should visit her doctor. More months passed, then serendipity lent a hand. Janet succumbed to flu and her family seized the opportunity. She felt poorly and so she readily agreed to them making an appointment for her.

Accompanied by a sister and one of her nieces, Janet found herself sitting opposite her doctor. Clearly she was a woman who was unwell, but he could not help but notice how she appeared not to know why she needed to see him. She appeared bemused and preoccupied. Questioning revealed little for her conversation was sparse. Without doubt she had flu, but in his opinion he thought Janet was also suffering from depression. He told them to reflect on what Janet had been through. She had lost her mother, had moved home and then within a year she had retired. He told them that these had evidently been major stressful life events, and while they occurred five years ago Janet had not adjusted as well as had been thought, and now she was reaping the emotional consequences.

Her doctor's diagnosis was to be expected. As we saw with Grace (chapter one), often when people in middle age or early old age first present with signs of dementia they are misdiagnosed with depression. The signs – poor concentration, forgetfulness, apathy and disinterest – are similar, and dementia is not expected at such a relatively young age. It is a diagnosis worth considering if for no other reason than it needs to be eliminated, for dementia can only be diagnosed through a process of excluding all else.

Janet was prescribed anti-depressants. For close to three months her doctor persisted with the diagnosis, until one day he raised the spectre of dementia. He did not think it was. Janet was still reasonably young and old age is when dementia is most commonly observed. On balance he still felt Janet was suffering from a major depressive episode that was resistant to treatment. He felt, however that the best course of action was for Janet to be referred to the "old age psychiatry service".

It was to be this family's misfortune that they lived in a part of the country where access to the service was founded on one profession, psychiatry. It was not the profession itself that was of concern; simply that no one profession can be the fount of all knowledge. Often, as in this instance, to be reliant on one profession is also to rely on one person. The result is inevitable delay and inefficiency. Caseloads are finite, and waiting times for appointments lengthen remorselessly. If Janet's case had been considered urgent the psychiatrist would have made a domiciliary visit and seen her within 72 hours. But it was not, so she was offered an outpatient's appointment – seven months in the future. The service wore the waiting time Janet and others had to endure as a badge of success, evidence of high demand for a valued service, rather than testimony to inefficiency and conspicuous failure to meet the needs of its patients.

While Janet waited to see the psychiatrist, a community psychiatric nurse (CPN) was allocated with responsibility to monitor. The CPN had little doubt that Janet was suffering from dementia. She warned the family to expect the worst. The months passed and Janet continued to deteriorate. It was not dramatic, nothing traumatic happened, but you could see how Janet was less aware of what was going on around her, less interested in others and more likely to do things for which there was no obvious reason.

When it came to the time for the psychiatrist to see Janet, I believe he said what he did because of what he saw.

Accompanying her were two exhausted sisters and maybe that is why nothing disastrous had happened. Janet was now at risk when alone: she would go out for no reason, occasionally getting lost but invariably returning to the house she had shared with her mother; the kitchen could be a particularly hazardous area and she would forget to close the back door. To manage her risky behaviour, someone from the family would sleep over at Janet's home most nights to keep a watchful eye on her. The psychiatrist said that he could not be certain what was wrong with their sister. It could be dementia, but what he would like to do would be to admit her to the assessment unit where he would be better able to understand what was going on. An accurate diagnosis could then be made and a care plan for the future agreed.

What I think he was really saying was "I'll give you respite", a break from the stress of caring for a woman who was increasingly vulnerable. He could not say, however when a bed would be available, the reason being that many assessment wards operate nowadays as 'holding stations'. They provide living space, not just for weeks, but sometimes for months and even years, for people who are admitted because their families can no longer cope with their wandering, shouting, aggression or any one of the other behaviours that trouble and exhaust family carers.

For over 20 years it has been well known that many family carers say "I can cope with what they can no longer do, but I cannot cope with what they have started to do". By this they mean they can cope with their partner or parent's dependency. They may never have imagined that a day would come when they would have to intimately care for their loved one, helping them wash, dress and use the toilet, taking responsibility for every aspect of their daily lives. They may have once doubted themselves, but so many families step forward and stoically accept what needs to be done, sustained by the knowledge that a relationship still remains even though it is now a relationship founded on dependency rather than reciprocity.

However, if their loved one starts to act in ways they have never done before and especially if it is beyond belief that they would ever have acted in this way, their behaviour is experienced as challenging and the capacity to care withers on the vine. This is not simply because the caring family lacks the skills to cope. It is more complex than that. An act of dependency such as needing to be dressed or helped with eating is circumscribed, time-limited, often predictable and once attended to is 'done'. There is a wonderful sense of relief that it is over – until next time. Acts of commission (what somebody does, rather than what they no longer do, which are acts of omission) such as abuse, calling out, repetitive questioning or persistently trying to leave home 'to go home' are challenging because the burden of care is in contrast endless and the impact is emotionally debilitating.

If the behaviour is also 'felt' to provide evidence that the person once known so well has departed, it becomes virtually impossible for a child or partner to devote themselves to the so-called '36-hour' day of care, a time of unremitting responsibility and constant supervision. To be able to dedicate oneself in this way a caring partner or child needs to know they are looking after a person they have known and loved for years. If the belief is that they are caring for a stranger or simply a shell that is playing host to symptoms of disease the behaviour is likely to exasperate and anger and many will find it difficult to cope. In such circumstances care at home will eventually collapse and the person with dementia is admitted either to a hospital or a care home. Unsurprisingly, if a person is admitted first to hospital a return home is unlikely. Because finding a place in a care home can be difficult, the outcome is often that they stay, some might say languish, on a ward for ages.

Janet waited for over three months before she was admitted to hospital for 'assessment'. Nearly two years had elapsed since her family first became troubled by her shabby appearance. She arrived passive and withdrawn with little intelligible speech.

Eleven weeks later it was tragic to see. She was violent, abusive and destructive. She spat, hit, kicked and screamed. In the beginning her family visited in droves, then they hardly came. If you caught one of the family on one of their fleeting infrequent visits and asked "How do you think your aunt is doing?", you knew what they were going to say. "What do you mean, how do you think our aunt is doing? That's not our aunt. If you had known our aunt she was a lovely gentle woman. Was it not only two nights ago that you contacted us to let us know that she had attacked another patient who had ended up in casualty with a fractured wrist? Have you not got two nurses off sick, injured when our aunt lashed out at them when they tried to stop her leaving the ward? We've spoken to the psychiatrist. He's told us that he never really had any doubt that she had dementia. This terrible disease has destroyed our aunt. That is why we hardly visit. We would rather remember her as she once was."

Ronald Reagan suffered with dementia for many years. Towards the end, his biographer Edmund Morris summed up his sentiments in The New Yorker, "For all the intimate familiarity of that face and body.... I did not feel his presence beside me, only his absence." It is not difficult to understand why Janet's family felt similarly, but were they right to assert that their aunt had disappeared? Was the psychiatrist correct to give the clear impression that the reason why Janet was acting this way was because she had dementia? Or should the clinical team have asked the family a simple question that would have illuminated Janet's plight? If they had asked it they would have found out why Janet was behaving the way she was. But they never did. It never crossed their mind to do so, so wrapped up were they in the belief that "dementia explains all".

Too often the tragic fate of people with dementia is that once they have been diagnosed with dementia everything that happens after the diagnosis is attributed to the diagnosis! Not just the dissolution of memory and intelligence but everything the person does. The pursuit of 'why' is rendered redundant, for the answer is already known – 'it is because they have dementia'. This is rarely so. Yet it is not simply because families assert that this is not their loved one that too many professionals are seduced by the simplicity of the disease model. It is also because the person is nothing like 'normal' people – they smear faeces, 'eat' inedible objects, expose themselves in front of others, hit people for no reason. People do not do such things. The result is that their behaviour places them outside the human constituency, and the 'disease model' finds a receptive audience.

So what was the question that should have been asked? It was simply, "Why had Janet never left home?" If that question had been asked they would have found out that Janet had always been shy and insecure. Timid and lacking confidence, she often felt awkward and ill-at-ease in the company of people she didn't know. Unsure of herself, she was never going to strike out into the big wide world. This quiet and reserved woman constructed for herself an unadventurous world, and within it she flourished. She was happy with who and what she knew. When her mother died she moved to within two streets from where her brother lived. She was destined to never change.

Tragically, when she was at her most vulnerable, when she no longer knew what was going on around her, when she was devoid of all insight and could no longer communicate her fears and insecurities, she found herself in a place we can barely comprehend. On the hospital ward, Janet would be sat in the lounge with people she not only did not know, but who probably simply by their presence terrified her. She would have looked out through disbelieving eyes at people who paced back and forward, plucked imaginary objects of the floor, who walked over to her, spoke incomprehensibly, moved her possessions, touched her clothes, called out, banged on windows, placed themselves on the floor, removed their clothes, urinated in front of her, and Janet would have had no idea why she should be there.

Would we stay? Would we feel safe? How often do we hear people with dementia pleading to go home? By 'home' they don't necessarily mean a physical place – often the word is used as a metaphor to express a desperate need to be out of harm's way and safe again.

Janet, that shy and timid woman, insecure and lacking confidence, was not staying. She was going home. But each and every time she reached the door she would find it protected by a digital lock. "You cannot have patients simply walking off." Was it little wonder that she was driven to acts of extreme desperation for not only was she in the company of people who frightened her, she was incomprehensibly trapped? The reassuring words of nurses ran contrary to all Janet saw and felt. She would always have acted with panic if her sheltered world had been turned upside down but it never was until she was at her most vulnerable and least able to cope, and then she acted with a ferocity that contradicted all that was known about her.

Once the question had been asked, what was obvious was that Janet's violent behaviour had little to do with disease and everything to do with a woman being true to herself and living a "kind of psychological pain whose persistence and intensity we can scarcely envisage" (Tom Kitwood).

Janet has now reached a sort of calm. The agony has healed. Her time on the hospital ward has been forgotten, but that is not to diminish the trauma she experienced. For people with dementia it is the 'here and now' that sustains their emotional health, not their past or future. If the moment happens to be a living hell to them then that is their life. All else has ceased to exist and an experience that is forgotten does not take away the pain that was felt. How Janet found a better emotional place will have to wait, however, until the story of Penny K (chapter 22).

PART II
Challenges as windows

"A disease is never a mere loss or excess – there is always a reaction, on the part of the affected organism or individual, to restore, replace, to compensate for and to preserve its identity, however strange the means may be."
– OLIVER SACKS

SEVEN

"I've done this before"

"Am I doing the right thing? I've lived here so long." Moira was troubled, as were her children. She was about to move house and she appeared overwhelmed by it all. She would talk over and over again about whether it was the right decision. She would agree that it was. Living alone, rattling around in a large house was not good for her. It compounded her sense of loneliness. It was also costly. But within days, sometimes hours, she would be telephoning her son or daughter again, fretting and unsure. Moira had always been so confident. She was also an intelligent woman. Now 73, over 50 years ago she had been a student at Oxford University, a remarkable achievement for a young woman in post-war Britain. It was a time so rife with prejudice and exclusion that only a few entered university, let alone scaled the heights of an Oxbridge education. Without fear of contradiction Moira was truly exceptional. Her children agreed and this was why they were so worried.

Prompted by her son, she visited her GP. Tearfully she confided she had lost confidence. She wasn't coping well. She kept forgetting what she planned to do next, what she had told someone and where she had put things, and there was a lot of that going on at the moment for she was packing up her possessions ready to move. Sometimes she could not remember what she had decided to keep or throw away. She would spend fruitless hours searching for a treasured memento before remembering that she had decided she didn't really want it anymore and more than likely it was already on the council tip having been put in the dustbin days ago.

Her GP was not particularly concerned for this was a stressful and emotional time for Moira, but as much to reassure her children as to assuage any worries she might have had I was asked to see her. The GP had written: *"increasing short term memory loss... she will forget things she has set off to do, she feels muddled and this is causing her great cause for concern... I feel it is appropriate to refer her for an objective memory and cognitive assessment just in case she ought to be considered for active treatment, although my overall impression is probably she is merely experiencing the short term memory loss that comes with stress, worry and advancing age."*

Moira was courteous, eloquent and grateful that I had given up the time to visit her at home. She was charming and I immediately developed a soft spot for her. As we talked I was also not unduly concerned. In conversation she never lost the thread or repeated herself. Examination of her memory revealed a few problems with the recall of what was new, but all else was fine. This test result was consistent with her absent-mindedness in daily life. However, there was a need for perspective. In a person's later years even when a decision has been made to remember, memory can be less efficient than it once was. Not impaired as such, but vulnerable to 'tip-of-the-tongue' experiences. Stress and age were the likely culprits, and I reassured Moira.

A year passed and I received another letter from Moira's GP: *"she has always been highly independent and competent... there has been quite a dramatic deterioration in the last six months. She recently got on the wrong train when travelling to London and ended up in Manchester... she recounted an odd episode when she was convinced her son and daughter-in-law were in the house and were redecorating a bedroom."*

She remembered me and again greeted me warmly, but Moira now displayed that loss of 'half an inch'. She was trying but just failing to succeed. There was a semblance of normality, but nothing felt quite right. She was living in her new home, but it was dismal and felt bleak. Moira was appropriately dressed, but would she normally have worn that skirt with those shoes? Her hair had been combed through but that was all. Letters were scattered on the table in the kitchen, but the envelopes had been dropped onto the floor where they remained, crumpled and abandoned. Moira also came across as vulnerable and haunted.

Moira wasn't sure whether her memory was worse, although she thought it might be. More troubling for her was that she, her home and her life just didn't feel right. She found this difficult to explain. This she also found upsetting for she had always been articulate with a rich and sophisticated vocabulary. "Have I told you that I studied English at university? You wouldn't think it now, would you?" During our conversation she made this self-deprecatory comment four times.

Moira's problem was still her poor memory. She struggled trying to recall what day it was and she talked about getting lost when on holiday in Germany with her daughter. All else – her concentration, thinking, language and perception – was within the range of normality. The prospect was that Moira's forgetfulness had evolved into mild cognitive impairment (MCI), a benign non-progressive state of exaggerated absent-mindedness. However, we needed to be watchful. Forty per cent of people with MCI are diagnosed as having Alzheimer's disease within three years and there was an alarm bell that was ringing hauntingly in the background. While Moira's decision-making was sound and in conversation she spoke fluently, I was meeting with a very intelligent woman. Were her current abilities normal for her? Could it be that while she scored above the thresholds of impairment the intellectual heights she had once scaled were giving a false impression of what the future might hold?

Distressingly the future was, within months, to be an obvious dementia. I met with her son who found it difficult to accept what was happening. "I lost my father 17 years ago, and now I'm losing my mother... Seventy-four isn't old." It was upsetting for Moira because she was aware that her memory was letting her down, that her judgement was poor and she felt vulnerable: "Sometimes I simply want to climb into a hole and hide away." She was frightened of being alone. Moira had got used to the loneliness that followed the death of her husband. Both her children lived far away, and her son in particular travelled the world on business. Yet now loneliness washed over her in painful waves. The fear, however, was completely new and it was a visitor with whom she did not wish to share her life. Moira doubted herself. She felt out of control. What silly mistakes might she have made but could not recall? Were the doors locked, had she left a window open? Might there have been something she had intended to do, maybe needed to do, but then had forgotten? At home she no longer felt safe, but there was nowhere else to go, no one to talk to. Then the delusions and hallucinations started.

Months earlier the GP's referral had mentioned that odd episode when she was convinced her son and his wife were in her bedroom, but now her neighbours were alarmed when Moira began knocking on their front doors asking whether they had seen her son and daughter. At other times she would be seen roaming the street searching, on occasions frantically calling out their names. Twice the police were called. Her GP prescribed a major tranquillizer, in other words an anti-psychotic drug, to calm and dampen down her delusions. A community psychiatric nurse was already visiting weekly, but now support workers were asked to check daily on her welfare and help with cooking and shopping. Around the house, on the settee, on the dining chairs, on a stool next to the telephone they found Moira had placed photographs of her son and daughter. Not of them as young children, but as they were today. Similarly, when she had been outside searching she was not looking for her children, young and vulnerable, but as the adults they now were. This was not typical of the confusion we see in dementia when memories from long ago become a restored reality and it is their past the person relives.

When asked why she had placed photographs of her children on chairs she quietly said, "Where else would they sit?" Without hesitation she admitted, "Of course we talk. Why would you not want to talk to your children?" Not only talk. At times the table was laid for three. In the kitchen, food Moira had cooked for her family remained congealed and blackened in saucepans, casserole dishes or under the grill. Plates were arranged nearby but the food had never been served.

Around 20% of people with Alzheimer's disease suffer from hallucinations and delusions (although many more are mistakenly said to be so when they are in fact misinterpreting what is going on around them). While they are terrified by what they see and know, others are alarmed by what they see and hear. Unsurprisingly, treatment with major tranquillizers is common. However, Moira's behaviour did not change. Yes, she was more sluggish and her thinking was not as sharp, but she was still talking to her photographs, sometimes cooking for them all and on occasions still walking the streets searching.

I started to meet regularly with Moira and it was sad to see her trying to hold onto the remnants of her life. Some days I would arrive and there would be a pot of tea and a delicious spread of little cakes on the table. I knew these were for us to eat because every day she would check her calendar to see who would be visiting. As she talked about "my indescribable, unimaginable life" she would at times break down. She once held my gaze and plaintively said, "I forget, but I still feel." Home alone, scared and fearful for the future, could it be that talking to her treasured photographs provided her with comfort and reassurance and thus she was not hallucinating at all. Instead, were her actions fuelled by insecurity and separation from those she cared most about? By 'sitting' them around the house she was fulfilling what she wished for most, to be a close family again, no longer separated by distance and time.

"Moira, when you talk to the photographs do you believe they are your children?"

"No, they're my photographs, but they're real to me."

"Real?"

"Yes, real. They're real. They don't say anything, but I know. I know what they're saying."

"How do you know?"

"Because they are my children. I'm their mother. I know them, they know me... I know they do".

"Do they say what you want to hear?"

She gave me a knowing look. "No, not always... but then I realise what they're saying is right. Life can't always be as you would like, but talking helps, so does listening", and she smiled. And then I was taken aback. I had been carried along by what I was being told, and it had not occurred to me to ask an obvious question. Moira 'answered' it anyhow. "I've done this before." Sixty years before.

Moira was 14 years old when her father had died. She talked about her devastation. How she would spend hours crying in her bedroom. Feeling alone, yearning for the presence of a gentle, quietly spoken man to whom she had been so close. He had been her confidant. Who would comfort her now? "I put a photograph of my father next to my bed. It rested against my bedside light, no lamp. I took it to school. I kept it in my blazer pocket and I'd look at it. I imagined him talking to me and I felt better, but sad. It was mixed because he wasn't really with me." Sixty years on, faced with unimaginable fears, Moira survived as an impressive human being. "Historically, as narratives – we are each of us unique," wrote Oliver Sacks – and while history rarely repeats itself, it does sometimes rhyme.

Why had Moira not acted in a similar way when her mother died, or more intriguingly when her husband died from lung cancer when only 59 years old? Because it was only when insecurity and self doubt overwhelmed her that she had the need. At another time, in another place, she once again needed the presence of those to whom she was closest and she comforted herself by talking not to her father, but to her children. She had not "gone round the bend" but when at her lowest, her mind, now compromised by memory that was failing and reasoning that was suspect, would play a cruel trick and what she wished for most became real, and the searching started. At other times the blurring of the boundary between reality and imagination was simply a comfort. These were not hallucinations and delusions but the actions of a woman holding onto her son and daughter as she had done once before when as a grieving teenager she yearned to be close to her father.

&

EIGHT

The madness of Mrs O

Mrs O is the most violent woman I have encountered. Living in a care home, she terrified the staff who cared for her. When I met her she was 75 and suffering from severe dementia. After her husband died she had lived alone for several years until self-neglect and increasingly risky behaviour led to her being admitted to the dementia care unit of a residential care home. From the first day she was a cause for concern. She was also a puzzle. Some of her carers thought she was madness personified.

She would walk around the home rarely displaying awareness of her surroundings. Most days she would sit contentedly, often smiling at passers by, her nodding barely perceptible, occasionally gesturing with her hand. She would participate, albeit passively, in activities. In essence, she conveyed an aura of kindliness.

Grossly disorientated and with no coherent speech, she was highly dependent on those who cared for her and at such times Mrs O was transformed beyond recognition.

Helping her out of bed, assisting her with dressing and washing (staff had long given up trying to give her a bath) were all met with unbridled ferocity. She was labelled as uncooperative and violent, her behaviour dismissed as typical of advanced dementia. "That's what the psychiatrist wrote," I was told by a senior carer, "a non-cognitive behavioural symptom of dementia. Although I think sometimes she's just mad."

Helping Mrs O in the toilet caused greatest concern. Labelled by many staff as incontinent, she was in fact as continent as those who cared for her. She was rarely found wet in her bed or chair. Instead she would be discovered walking around soiled, most probably after having failed to find the toilet. Staff would find wet clothing hidden away, such was her embarrassment. However, helping her in the toilet, checking to see if her clothing was soiled, and attempting to change her wet clothes caused Mrs O immense distress.

Her screams could be heard throughout the home. She would punch, slap, scratch and spit. Her assaults on staff often degenerated into struggles. Two carers would invariably be involved. While this made the situation 'manageable' it in no way reduced the trauma of the experience. However, the catalyst for understanding what was going on in the mind of Mrs O was not her toileting but turned out to be her ulcerated legs.

Her leg ulcers had been a problem while she lived at home. District nurses visited daily to clean and dress them. All the reports suggested that she enjoyed these visits. Not only was there no record of violent or distressed behaviour, the notes documented how "chatty" and "jolly" she seemed. "Pleasantly confused" was a term that was often used, although whenever that phrase is heard I think it is right for us to say, "Pleasant for whom?" Not for the person with dementia, but for those who are caring.

In the care home the senior carers who had responsibility for changing her dressings were met with the same violent conduct that was encountered when trying to help her during toileting. Yet the district nursing reports described how in the weeks before Mrs O came into the care home she had been assisted in the toilet with no upset or difficulty at all. What had happened to the woman who just a few months ago had been so pleasant and accommodating?

The disease-centred model offered a ready solution. Dementia is progressive. Clearly she was now more disoriented, dependent, disinhibited, and generally more difficult. Yet as we have already seen, and will continue to see in other stories, to ascribe everything people do to the underlying pathology is a flawed explanation.

As we saw in part one, the problem is not just abuse or maltreatment, but also unthinking, unfeeling and insensitive care that is embraced by Tom Kitwood's term 'malignant social psychology' – actions so subtle they pass as 'unseen' by carers who commit them but nevertheless easily result in 'aggressive resistance' during intimate care. Was Mrs O reacting to poor care practice? It appeared not. In this home, care was sensitive and respectful. Dressings were changed in the privacy of her bedroom; toilets doors would always be closed. Staff smiled, offered gentle encouragement and simple explanations. They understood that in the briefest passage of time these explanations would be lost and so they would repeat regularly what had been said. While it was likely that Mrs O rarely understood let alone remembered what she heard, she drew no comfort from the staff's gentle ways. Eye contact, soft tone of voice and reassuring gestures had no effect.

Her only child, Rita, visited the home maybe twice a week. She might have come more often if her mother's behaviour had not so upset her. Her mother had always been a moral, somewhat reserved woman. Rita had read about 'disinhibition' (the loss of inhibitions), yet she still found it difficult to reconcile her mother's abusive and violent behaviour with the woman she had always known. As she came to trust staff she talked of her strict upbringing. Despite being a teenager in the liberated 'swinging sixties', boyfriends were only grudgingly accepted, her skirts were long, heels low and there were set times to be back home which always seemed too early. There was no malice in her mother; she was simply concerned and unfailingly protective.

Mrs O had married late for her generation. She had stayed at home until she was 30, when she married the 'man from the Pru' – the insurance man who dealt with her mother's affairs. She was pregnant within a year.

Rita rarely saw her parents being physically affectionate with each other – although her mother was never slow to give her a hug and a cuddle – but she never doubted that her mother loved her father deeply. It was simply that she couldn't show it. She gained the impression that her parents were not sexually intimate. There was the odd grumble from her father, an occasional snide comment and of course she was an only child.

Life at home was unremarkable. They were a family

quietly and somewhat conservatively living their lives in post-war suburbia. These were the years of austerity and 'make do and mend' was the philosophy of the day; Mrs O was never to forsake her frugal ways. Nothing out of the ordinary ever happened, except that as a child Rita was mystified why she rarely saw her aunts and uncles, her mother's brothers and sisters "for Dad was an only child like me". It wasn't that they were simply remote; it was more the fact that as a subject they were clearly off limits. Except for Uncle Harry, her mother's elder brother. He was in regular contact, but she hardly ever saw Maisie, Doris and Phil, her mother's younger siblings. Whenever they were all together invariably at "an awful family gathering", there was always tension in the air. Nothing was said, yet the absence of words said much more.

Harry still figured in his sister's life for he would visit most days. The others never came. More often than not Harry would be seen holding his sister's hand, occasionally shedding a tear. He was often overheard softly saying, "I'm sorry, pet. I know I've let you down." What staff read into this was that Harry only lived a short distance from the care home, alone in a large house. And that's where Mrs O should be living, with him. Harry knew of her troubles and how many of the staff felt about her. He felt guilty. He had let her down. Harry was being too hard on himself, but it made sense.

One day our visits coincided. Harry had become particularly upset and he was being comforted in a side room when I arrived. The home manager wondered whether I'd like to have a word with him. And our words were to uncover the reason for his sister's behaviour.

I had expected to be talking with a man distressed by the sight of his sister's advanced dementia and overwhelmed by a sense of guilt for not taking her into his home at her time of greatest need. Guilt was to the fore but not for the reason we thought. He started to tell me how he had let her down and I was about to say there was no need, he was being too hard on himself, then out of the blue he said, "Because I always knew it was true." His pitiful refrain had nothing to do with his sister's dementia.

The words tumbled out for he could no longer hold back what had been tormenting him for years. As a child Mrs O had been subject to sexual abuse at the hands of her father. Their mother was protective of her vulnerable daughter, yet she also colluded with her husband's vile ways and ensured the matter was never spoken about. But Harry knew the truth because he had been there. He had seen. He had heard his little sister sobbing. So had his older brother (killed when a young man in the Second World War) but nothing was said. Even when the family turned against her, Harry remained silent.

As Harry told his story he spoke of his sister's special 'uncle'. A neighbour they might see when out who was attentive to the little girl, but who Harry could only ever recall speaking to their mother. He never visited their home and Harry could never remember seeing him with his father. Was Mrs O a 'love-child', a constant reminder of his wife's infidelity against whom her tormented 'father' acted out his bitterness?

The conspiracy of silence ensured the younger brothers and sisters never knew. To them Dad was Dad and they loved him. As she grew up, I daresay feeling unclean and unworthy, Mrs O held her silence. When she was 13 her father died. One day she must have confided in her sisters. "Stories, just evil, nasty stories. That's what they thought and we said nothing," said Harry. Insecure, shy, uncomfortable with boys, her teenage years were unhappy. If she ever dared to speak about the abuse she was accused of sullying the memory of their father. As she entered her twenties she was seen as the sexually frustrated spinster still telling her malicious lies, and Harry and their mother continued to keep their silence. Eventually Mrs O was ostracized by her family. Except for Harry, who knew but never said. This was the family rift Rita had always suspected.

Now affected by dementia, the world of Mrs O must have been bewildering. In the care home, staff tried to bring down the barrier between themselves and the people they cared for by not wearing uniforms. They also aspired to respect their residents' dignity. Intimate care was conducted in the privacy of bedrooms. The use of toilets was preferred to commodes. Yet what did this hold in store for Mrs O? When the dressings on her ulcerated legs needed to be changed she would be taken by a care worker – but in the eyes of Mrs O a stranger – to the privacy of her room that she may or may not have recognised, sat on or by her bed, her skirt would be lifted and her stockings rolled down. Can you imagine what she may have thought was going to happen next?

Dementia had devastated her reasoning, her recall of daily experience, even the ability to understand the reassuring words of those who cared for her, but it had not taken away her soul. This had not been surrendered to disease. She was an abused child, the experience of which was no longer tempered by the passage of time. She was unable to say to herself "I was abused 70 years ago" for the intervening times had descended into an abyss of lost and irretrievable memories. Hence she reacted with a ferocity that was out of proportion to all that was happening around her, for her fears were founded on abusive experiences that were no longer consigned to remote history.

To be taken to the toilet was equally distressing. Possibly agnosic (unable to recognise things properly) with no awareness of her dependency on others, her experience was to be in a small room with one, sometimes two people who were attempting to remove her clothes. Is it any wonder she fought back?

The reason why Mrs O had enjoyed the visits of the district nurses and had never resisted their intimate care was not because she was less ravaged by dementia then, but because she was less threatened. The nurses had turned up in uniform. Their manner was efficient and clinical and there was little chance for the mist of confusion to generate misunderstanding and fear.

To test this hypothesis we asked whether the district nurses would visit the residential home to take responsibility for changing her dressings again. They agreed to do so for six weeks and during that time not once did Mrs O fight them off. The uniform took away the ambiguity and she felt safe. However, having demonstrated Mrs O's behaviour was to do with mystery and threat and not simply 'dementia', what was to be done when the care staff again picked up responsibility? They were not going back into uniform for the sake of one resident, even though we argued that the barriers that can develop between staff and the people they care for are more to do with 'hearts and minds' than anything as tangible as a uniform.

Instead we resurrected the rarely used treatment room that was now doubling as a storeroom and filled it with 'cues' to help Mrs O understand the context. In went a metal trolley, first-aid box, bandages and ointments. Its use was lost on no one for it reeked of a hospital casualty department. The room had an unambiguous purpose and this was the objective. As dementia progresses and powers of understanding fail, interior design messages should be clear and impact on as many senses as we can. Known as 'organised space as stimulus' an example is a dining room where the clatter of knives and forks, the smell of food, and the sight of crockery, table cloths and sauce bottles all declare 'this is where I eat.'

When Mrs O's dressings needed to be changed she was no longer taken to the privacy of her bedroom. Instead she was taken to the treatment room and even though the carers remained out of uniform the cues were so clear and powerful she was reassured that all was well. Peace of mind, so important to us all but too often neglected in the care of people with dementia had displaced panic and dread.

However, this left the challenge of helping Mrs O in the toilet, an event that would happen maybe up to six times a day. We drew on the lessons we had learned and went against 'best practice'. Rather than take Mrs O to the privacy of a toilet, the use of which is consistent with the need to preserve dignity and respect at a time of intimate dependency, we placed a commode in the treatment room behind a screen. When a visit to the toilet was scheduled

Mrs O would be taken to the treatment room, sat by the trolley, cued into the 'clinical' experience and only then would she be walked over to the commode. Reassured by the abundant cues, as well as the gentle caring tones of her keyworkers, her behaviour revealed how she felt. No anger, no violence, simply benign acceptance.

This is not to say all was perfect in Mrs O's world. It never had been, nor would it be now. There were still outbursts when she was taken to use the commode, but these were few and far between, and tended to occur when staff were too rushed to cue her into the 'clinical experience' and instead walked her straight behind the screen. There were also the challenges of assisting Mrs O out of bed and helping her to dress, undress and wash. However, whenever possible her intimate care would be displaced to the reassuring setting of the treatment room and more often than not she would calm.

What also changed was how staff now regarded Mrs O: no longer mad, bad or simply demented, but as a frightened woman with a tragic history trying to survive in a world she barely understood. A valuable lesson was learned. When caring for people with dementia you cannot have inflexible ways of working. People's histories, habits and horrors are too complex for this to be so. If care is to be truly person-centred, it sometimes means going against current thinking in order to help a person live their life free of torment and foreboding. I don't think Mrs O would disagree.

&

NINE

Mrs S had fallen far

I originally wrote about Mrs S in the *Journal of Dementia Care* for her unique story helped usher in a person-centred understanding of challenging behaviour. Aged 75, she was admitted to a care home suffering with dementia. At home her self-care skills had been wonderfully resistant to the savagery of Alzheimer's disease, but she had become more and more muddled in her thinking and unacceptably risky in what she did. The final straw occurred when, having been told not to use the cooker, she placed a saucepan in the microwave oven. The explosion set off the smoke alarm and resulted in Mrs S agitatedly banging on her neighbours' front door crying out that her house was on fire.

Mrs S had had little schooling, but throughout her life she had always come over as refined and genteel, a 'lady' to all who knew her. An assistant in a baker's shop and tearoom, she had the good fortune to marry the owner's son. To keep up with the airs and graces of her formidable and sharp tongued mother-in-law – who was not particularly pleased by her son's choice of wife – Mrs S embarked upon a journey to become as sophisticated and cultured as her husband's mother. Not quite the story of *My Fair Lady* but not that far removed.

The great sorrow for her daughters was now to observe the unravelling of their mother's sophistication and the destruction of her personal standards. Compared to other residents she had an excellent social façade, but she had fallen far. "What's happening to our mother is unimaginable. She never would have wanted to be like this. We miss her so much because this isn't her." Both sisters struggled to accept the decline in their mother's personal hygiene that dramatically gathered apace when she entered the residential home.

From her first day in the home, Mrs S was regularly found wet while walking around. At night she would on occasions discreetly soil herself and then 'parcel' the faeces in her clothes or bed linen and hide the evidence under the bed or in drawers. The rapid deterioration in their mother's behaviour was explained to her daughters in terms of the progressive nature of dementia and the difficulty people with dementia have coping with change. The word 'incontinence' was mentioned. Very soon she was seen as difficult, for Mrs S showed no interest in using the two toilets provided for the residents. She was often seen walking into the toilets and within moments walking out or pausing, looking in and then walking on. When found with wet or soiled clothes later she would deny this had happened.

It was eventually decided that she was not incontinent but wilfully choosing not to use the toilet. Her daughters were told, "Some do become difficult." The decision was taken to place Mrs S on a three-hour toileting programme in which she was prompted and accompanied to the toilet. Her response was simply not to co-operate. Staff could get Mrs S to the toilet but she would then steadfastly refuse to use it. Within three weeks Mrs S had become depressed. Apathetic and disinterested, she would say little, would never join in activities and would wet herself wherever she sat. The outcome was the same although her motivation was now clearly different – but what had motivated Mrs S to wet herself in the first place?

Functional analysis is the pursuit of finding out 'why' people behave in the way they do. People, whether they have dementia or not, rarely do things without reason. Sometimes we may have to ask ourselves "Why did I say that, why did I act in that way?", and while we may not always like what we find out about ourselves, there will have been a reason. Similarly a person with dementia has reasons for what they do, so while Mrs S was unable to tell us why she was acting the way she was, that did not mean there was no explanation to seek.

For nine weeks Mrs S was dismissed as aggressive and incontinent. Little happened to improve her life. Her daughters, one in particular, were visiting less and less. Clearly despairing and unable to relate to what was unfolding before their eyes, they sought pleasure in their memories.

One day I was visiting the home to arrange a series of training sessions on person-centred care when I found myself gazing down at a woman holding Mrs S's hand. She explained that her mother was a parody of who she had been. She was both bewildered and outraged at what was happening. She explained that she had learnt to cope when her mother had difficulty remembering and did silly things. It was frustrating and at times exhausting, but it got easier and easier as she appreciated what her mother was going through. Now it was different. This person she was visiting bore little resemblance to her mother. She cared little for herself, and it had all happened so quickly, within days of coming into the home.

Mrs S had been vain, often self-righteous and on occasions insufferably conceited. "Mum always dreaded growing old because appearances were everything, especially the way she looked."

I was told how her vanity was nourished by weekly visits to the hairdressers, how her make-up always had to be perfect, and as for bags and shoes, "She had so many our dad despaired, but that's the way mum was. He didn't really mind, but her hang ups about personal hygiene, that was different. She was obsessed. He would get really wound up, especially if it made him late. You see mum could never use a toilet that wasn't ours. I don't just mean a public lavatory; she couldn't even use a friend's toilet." And with that a window into Mrs S's world opened.

What had Mrs S been expected to do during the toileting programme? To use what were in essence two public lavatories. It did not matter that the staff did their utmost to keep them clean: Mrs S's behaviour was articulating an aversion to shared toileting arrangements that she had never been able to accept. It was a distaste that was fostered and elaborated upon during her metamorphosis into the polished and cultivated woman she became, but the roots of which were located in her earliest years.

Our early years, of which we have little or no memory, are a time rich in promise, but also a time of learning, decisions and discoveries that make us who we are today. Both the Jesuits and Sigmund Freud saw the child as being parent to the adult. However, the lessons we learned and the adventures embarked upon are mostly beyond our recall. The currents of who we have become run deep and often unseen beneath the everyday flow of words and deeds, and if we try to trace their origins we reach a time beyond which nothing is remembered. When asked, most people say their earliest memory is when they were around four years of age. Before then how much can we remember? By definition, nothing: this is the period of 'pre-memorial' experience. We cannot recall our toilet training, our 'terrible twos', nor any experiences that mean today we are trusting and confident, or the opposite.

What happens prior to our earliest accessible memories is laid down as personal truth. It is just what we know about ourselves, the way we are. The question is can we forget that which is not remembered? Can we lose that which has not been laid down as an accessible memory trace? The answer is, in all likelihood, no. Hence these early experiences and lessons remain part of who we are, exercising their influence but forever inaccessible.

Mrs S would have been toilet trained by the age of three. She would have been encouraged to toilet privately, hygienically and with dignity, and once she had mastered the skill of continence never again would she choose to wet or soil herself. Yet she would have no memory of learning this lesson and no recall of the pleasure she would have given her parents when she used the toilet or her potty appropriately and, equally significant, the pride she felt in herself for having pleased her parents. Clearly the green shoots of self respect are not to be found as we mature as young adults, but are laid down during a time of life of which we have no knowledge at all.

In our adult years so many of us are left feeling awkward when we have to ask "Where's the toilet?" in a place we do not know, ill at ease when using public lavatories and an unassailable and indisputable knowledge that to wet oneself is degrading. The lessons we learnt are no longer remembered, what is known is simply 'personal truth'.

For Mrs S, her need for hygiene had resulted in public lavatories becoming an anathema. Having walked in and walked out of the toilets she would embark upon a fruitless journey. She would never come across a toilet that felt right. It did not matter that she had been told that there were two communal toilets for her to use. Her inability to remember for more than moments rendered such information redundant. When unable to hold onto her urine any longer, she was compelled to wet herself where she stood. Can we imagine how degraded she must have felt at this moment? Humiliation would have fuelled her 'parcelling'.

It does not matter that Mrs S would not have been able to remember what she had done, for in the same way that we understood Janet's predicament (chapter 6) what is of utmost importance to people with dementia is the moment of their experience, the 'here and now'. Their memory problems means the experience cannot be tempered by recall of what has happened in the past nor a sense of what to expect next (for example, that the carers were and would always be kind and tolerant). When confronted later with the evidence of what she had done, of course she denied that she had wet herself, for Mrs S would not know of a time when she would have done so. When her bladder is full she goes to the toilet. That is her personal truth. She knows of no other way, of no other time.

Having understood, the first challenge was what could be done to lift Mrs S out of her depression. Her GP agreed and prescribed a course of anti-depressants. After three weeks her mood improved a little and she was more alert, but how were we to address the cause of her depression? First, the carers and I talked over our distaste for public lavatories. How so many of us avoid them whenever we can, mistrust the fact that they are used by strangers and are troubled by germs that lurk unseen. How we may take special precautions to avoid touching the toilet seat, the handle when flushing the toilet, the door handle and taps, and how we feel reassured when seat covers are available or sterile sprays or wipes are provided.

We then looked at whether the carers' use of the staff toilet said less about infection control and a wish to preserve the privacy of residents, and more about the cleanliness of the residents' toilets. If these toilets fell short of what we would want for ourselves there was a problem to be faced up to. The message was stark. If the communal toilets were not clean enough for those who worked in the care home, how could they be acceptable to those whose home this was? Were the staff unwittingly condemning people to wet and soil themselves, then to be wrongly labelled as incontinent or to be seen as having no regard for personal cleanliness when it was the opposite that was motivating their behaviour? Hearts and minds were changed, but what could be done on a practical level?

Despite Mrs S's suffering we all agreed that moving to a care home where there were en suite facilities would not be in her best interest. It was also satisfying to observe how staff attitudes had changed. There was a real determination to help Mrs S, if for no other reason than so many of the women caring for her now identified with her plight. There was no question of the home being able to provide an en suite toilet, nor could one of the toilets be hers and hers alone. We thought about putting in familiar and thus reassuring items that might resemble her toilet at home. Her daughters thought this was unlikely to work and anyhow there was the very real prospect that other residents would remove them, especially as one gentleman was always gathering and hoarding other people's possessions. Our options were limited so we concentrated on what causes most women the greatest concern, the toilet seat.

In both toilets we provided a brightly coloured disposable seat cover dispenser. While we anticipated that the dispenser would attract Mrs S's attention, we equally knew that she would be unable to learn or reason what she needed to do. There was no alternative but for staff to be observant. The layout of the building meant the toilets were prominent, and as they were also signposted, Mrs S would always seek and find the toilets. From now on if

109

staff saw her approaching or walking away from the toilet they would draw her attention to the dispenser and place a cover over the seat and then leave her be. Sixty per cent of the time it worked. At other times her disgust overcame our efforts to make the toilet acceptable. The solution was by no means perfect, but there was little doubt that, all round, Mrs S's life in the home improved. The staff were more benevolent in their attitude towards her, and once her mood lifted never again did she descend the depths of depression.

The truth is that Mrs S probably helped us more than we were ever able to help her, even though she was not able to know this was so. Mrs S's troubles were the beacon that opened the eyes of so many of us to the knowledge that people with dementia act in the same way as we all do. Each morning they awake, get on with their lives and do their best. We, baffled and bemused when they make errors, may wrongly believe we are grappling with symptoms of disease. Mrs S helped us realise how wrong we had been.

&

TEN

Rock man

I got to know Mr D after his wife sought me out at a
neighbourhood resource centre for families caring for
relatives with dementia. She told me about months of
increasing worry as her husband had become more
absent-minded and argumentative. "No one in the family
understands what's going on any more." His lapses of
memory were puzzling, and at times irritating, but of
greater concern were his strange remarks and his increasingly odd behaviour. There was an occasion when he
complained that it was not possible for him to open the
front door as he had a newspaper in one hand and a
briefcase in the other. She had noticed how he hesitated
when he crossed the road. But what had prompted her to
seek help were not her worries that had grown deeper
day by day, week by week, but a particular incident.

It had been the christening of their first grandchild.
They had been blessed with a glorious spring day. Family
and friends had come from far and wide. After the

ceremony everyone gathered at their daughter's for a cel-
ebratory lunch. As people took their places at the table
Mrs D heard her daughter ask, "Where's Dad?" She
realised that she hadn't seen him for what on reflection
seemed ages. Then she heard somebody say, somewhat
quizzically, "Isn't that him sitting outside in the car?" It
was. Walking towards him Mrs D remembered feeling
livid. Her husband was a private man. He liked his own
space and he had never enjoyed parties. Over the years
she had often seen him slip away. He might find a
bookshelf to browse, or if there was a garden to walk in
he would take a discreet stroll. Part of the problem was
that he was set in his ways. A stickler for routine, he felt
unsettled when life felt different, and as a consequence
holidays had always been few and far between. But this
was too much.

As she approached the car she was thinking he's done it
again, "He's listening to the radio. How can he be so anti-
social at the christening of his own grandchild?" Mrs D
knew her husband well enough to know he would never
normally be so insensitive, but that knowledge did not
prepare her for what she would hear. He demanded to go
home: "I am going home. I am going back for dinner and
if you don't get your things we'll be eating late."

At first staggered and disbelieving, and then exasperated, she pleaded with him to be sensible. But within his
tortured world he was already being so. It was not that he
could not recall why they were at their daughter's and
how important the day was. His determination to return
home reflected a desperate need to feel safe and secure –
not physically but psychologically. He did not wish to be

in an unfamiliar house and sit opposite people whose names he should know but could not remember; he did not wish to suffer the embarrassment of not knowing what to do next. He wanted to be comfortable among his familiar things doing what he knew.

Home offers routine and predictability. It is why so many people in the beginnings of their dementia spend so much time absorbed in putting things away and checking they are where they ought to be. They want life to be as it has always been but as recall fades they lose confidence in themselves so they need to check and then check again that all is where it should be. Mr D's personality was to ensure that his future was to be no different.

Over the following months, as his memory progressively worsened, he was diagnosed with probable Alzheimer's disease. The process had been rife with subterfuge for Mr D was never to acknowledge he had any problems. As far he was concerned there was nothing the matter, and any difficulties he might have were the fault of other people. He was, however, persuaded to retire and sell his chain of small supermarkets that were dotted around the side streets of the city.

Disoriented and dependent he exacted a heavy toll on his wife's welfare. She described him as a "born worrier" and so it was not surprising that as his daily life became more and more characterised by apprehension and insecurity he became increasingly agitated. Home care was offered as was day care but Mrs D refused. Mrs D felt that her husband would not accept the presence of strangers, nor would he take kindly to the mysteries of care. Her concerns were confirmed when the sole attempt to take Mr D to a daycare centre resulted in him becoming so anxious he tried to climb out of a window rather than stay in the company of people he did not know in a place he did not recognise.

Time passed and Mr D was to become one of the most tormented people with dementia I have ever worked with. As his wife struggled to cope there was to be a disturbing turn of events that led to Mr D being referred to as 'rock man'. A set of behaviours appeared that were to all but destroy the health of his devoted wife.

Day after day Mr D was driven to gather rocks and large stones from his front and rear gardens and store them in neat piles in his garage. From early morning to the end of the day he would work in the garden. Collecting his wheelbarrow and spade he would walk over to a flower bed and in his pursuit of rocks and stones he would systematically destroy it. Flowers, shrubs, bushes and small trees were pulled out or hacked down. He would then shovel as much soil as he could into his wheelbarrow and diligently wheel it onto the lawn where he would empty the contents. Separating the soil from the rocks and stones he would wheel his harvest into the garage and then return to the garden where he would gather up as much soil as his patience and judgement would allow and deposit it onto the flower bed.

He decimated both gardens. His wife pleaded with him to no avail. Efforts to stop him were met with anger and resistance. At times his hands were bloodied and bruised but he would not or could not stop. At the end of the day he would pace the house, ultimately to fall into an exhausted sleep.

For no reason we could identify, Mr D would at times vary his behaviour. Instead of wheeling his barrow onto the lawn he would bring it into the house and empty the contents wherever he saw fit. The hall and lounge carpets became damp, dirty and home to a huge number of bugs.

Eventually his behaviour escalated to the point where Mrs D not only struggled with her own bitterness and resentment – "Why me, why us? Why is he doing this to me?" – but she had to come to terms with the alarm and fury of neighbours, acquaintances and even strangers who happened to be walking by their house. Mr D would rush into the street to accost passers-by. Nobody could understand a word he was saying yet his face and tone of voice revealed the terror he felt. On occasions he would take it upon himself to go into his neighbours' gardens armed with his wheelbarrow and spade and descend upon their flowerbeds with the same meticulous savagery he had wrought in his own garden.

By no stretch of the imagination could Mr D be referred to as 'pleasantly confused'. Helpful suggestions hinged on a need to contain his behaviour. Sedation was regularly advised, as was telling Mrs D that enough was enough and that it would be best for all concerned if he went to live in an EMI (elderly mental infirm) unit. However, his wife would not let go, even though she constantly questioned whether it was still her husband with whom she was sharing a home. For Mrs D this was the bleakest of times. Helplessness and despair affected her terribly and to be told that it was all because her husband had dementia provided neither consolation nor hope for the future.

Watching Mr D's restless actions, observing his

tortured facial expressions and seeing how he ignored discomfort meant it was easy to feel his torment but this brought us no closer to understanding why he did what he was compelled to do day after day.

I don't believe Mrs D particularly enjoyed our conversations. For her they were pointless, but she was polite and always tolerant of my questions. We would rake over the coals of the past as I tried to connect the present to all she knew of her husband. Why were rocks and stones of such significance to him? Why was there a need to hide them away? I would tell her that I believed his behaviour was obscuring his psychology rather than providing us with a gateway to his world of needs and feelings. But for Mrs D it was just talking for the sake of talking, and possibly a source of regret as she was asked to reminisce about the fine upstanding man her husband had once been.

Mr D seemed to have become more insecure as he aged. Mrs D told me how hard her husband worked. He worked long hours six days a week. Up before dawn, he would return home late at night. He was always fretting that there were not enough hours in the day. He was not concerned with status or authority. His success was the result of wanting to bring his family the security and peace of mind that comes from wanting for nothing. While he could be remote, he was a dutiful husband and father. This was why Mrs D was so upset. If he knew the heartache and worry he was causing her and the children it would confirm what she so often heard others saying: this was not her husband. And if he did not know and he was living in an indescribable world of torment that we could neither reach nor resolve, then was it not wrong to prolong his suffering?

Mr D had always cherished his home. He had spent a great deal of money creating a beautiful house with gardens equally as splendid. "Why would he want to destroy what had meant so much to him? And I don't mean our marriage. He loved this house. Too much, sometimes. It was his haven, where he could always return when things got on top of him. Have you seen the bars on the downstairs windows? They're quite attractive but they're still bars. We had them put in after the attempted robbery at one of the shops. He couldn't bear to think that somebody might break in and take what was ours. Maybe even destroy something he treasured. Now he's doing it himself. How ironic is that?"

Mr D had dedicated his life to buying, accumulating and then managing his supermarkets to the highest standards. Throughout his life he had worried and been troubled by what many would have said was of little consequence. Possibly as a means of gaining respite from self-doubt, he developed an obsessional personality. If one is preoccupied with detail and punctuality there is little opportunity to dwell on and be affected by insecurities, inadequacies and perceived failings. While his dedication, dependability and eye for detail held him in good stead and had been the recipe for success, it was also to be his undoing.

You could set your clock by Mr D. On a Friday evening 15 years earlier he had closed one of his shops and was leaving the supermarket to bank the day's takings. This was something he would have done hundreds of times – at the same time of day, always alone – and unbeknown to him others had been watching. As he was closing the door of the shop, three youths ran across the road to snatch the money he had placed in a nondescript bag. But Mr D saw them coming. In a flash he was back in the shop and he slammed the door shut. He just had time to engage the lock as they crashed into the door.

As they hammered on the door Mr D ran through the shop to an office at the rear where he could telephone the police. Not prepared to give up, the youths ran to a builder's skip outside a nearby house that was being renovated. They grabbed a large fragment of masonry and threw it through the window of the shop. Clambering in they ran through the store toward Mr D who was trapped in an office, behind a door that he could not lock. Can we imagine how Mr D, a fretful and fearful man, must have felt in those moments as the youths charged towards him? This was to have been a quick robbery, over in seconds, but because of his actions his assailants were now enraged. What would they do to him? To his immense relief nothing happened. For reasons that never became clear, the youths hesitated, turned and ran off empty-handed.

Fifteen years on, Mr D continued to wrestle with his enduring need to be safe, but now his need was contaminated by his history, for his past intruded upon the present as if it was again painful reality. A distressing distant memory dominated his thinking and coloured his judgement. His need for security was now shaped by a shocking experience that happened 15 years ago, but as with Mrs O (chapter eight) the accompanying emotions were no longer tempered by the passage of time.

As I explained this to Mrs D she said, "You mean my husband's memory is playing tricks?" Not quite. I told her how Alzheimer's disease progressively destroys the brain tissue that contains our memory traces, memories that we draw on to help us interpret how we feel and what we see and hear. In dementia, recent memories are more likely to be lost first than more remote memories (this is known as Ribot's Law). As a result the understanding her husband brought to his world and which in turn motivated his behaviour was increasingly rooted in the past. Consequently, what happened years ago now provided Mr D with the facts that once again drove him to protect himself, his wife and his property. His impaired reasoning prevented him from appreciating that people rarely if ever attack your home with rocks and stones taken from your garden. But within the limits laid down by his intellectual disability, Mr D was behaving in a manner that was right and appropriate. He was not destroying what he cherished and treasured most of all. He was doing what he had done before: protecting his wife and home.

There was to be no successful resolution in terms of giving Mr D what he had never possessed, namely peace of mind. However, understanding not only drives us closer to finding solutions – it can also promote tolerance. With tolerance comes the potential to cope, even with situations that are basically unchanged.

This was to be the outcome for Mr and Mrs D. Once it was explained that her husband's behaviour was evidence that he remained the man she had known for years, but a man now tormented by a past trauma, Mrs D was better equipped to cope. She was no longer terrorised by a sense that he was deliberately acting to hurt or spite, nor was she drawn to the belief that she may be condemned to live with a person who she felt was not her husband despite the physical evidence to the contrary.

Mrs D and her husband went to his family's home in Ireland for a holiday, during which time their sons arranged for the gardens to be tidied and a secure gate to be placed at the end of the drive. The downstairs carpets were replaced and I advised Mrs D on their return to make sure that when her husband went into the gardens both the front and back doors were locked. The most damaging consequences of his conduct thus prevented, Mr D was able to continue his driven behaviour without interference.

I came to understand our efforts to help Mr D in terms of 'functional displacement'. Functional analysis identifies the function of, in other words the reason for, behaviour and interprets it as being meaningful. Functional displacement provides the person with an equivalent but more acceptable means of meeting their needs in a way that is neither as invasive nor as exasperating for carers to endure. For it to work, the alternative made available must be functionally equivalent (ie have the same meaning to the person) and not just be more acceptable to others (the story of Roger in chapter 19 shows how the approach can fail when what is encouraged does not possess the same meaning), it must not require more effort and it must be readily available for it is unlikely that the alternative pattern of behaviour will be learned.

In the case of Mr D we made sure that the functionally equivalent way of behaving was all that was to hand. The flower beds were cleared of large stones and a pile of small rocks and stones was placed next to the garden path. He would take his barrow, load it up with the stones and rocks and wheel it into the garage and store them as before. There were no demands to stop. His devastated speech and comprehension prevented us from verbally acknowledging his fears. Instead he was reassured by touch and smiles that his actions were okay; and sometimes helping him to gather the rocks appeared to calm him. As the pile diminished it was replenished from what had been stored in the garage and the pattern continued. Little had changed. Mr D remained motivated to protect what was his, but the consequences of his behaviour were now easier for Mrs D to tolerate.

Mrs D also derived comfort from the knowledge that as her husband's dementia progressed he would one day no longer recall the attempted robbery. It would be another memory swept away by Alzheimer's disease. Once this happened he would no longer be motivated to hide away rocks and stones, and the suffering she shared with her husband would be over. The suffering she was referring to was not the physical strain of caring: no, she was referring to the emotional pain she endured each day for she detested seeing her husband so distraught. And this is how the story unfolded.

Mr D continued to gather his harvest of stones and rocks for months until one day he appeared less determined and within the week Mrs D telephoned me to say that her husband was displaying no interest at all in the pile of stones that now lay untouched. She began to cry both with relief but also because while she had been waiting for this to happen she knew that it meant that a further piece of their life together had descended into the abyss of memories now lost forever.

Years passed and Mrs D, with the help of her children (who I believed had been touched by the way their father had cast a protective veil over their mother), continued to care for her husband at their home. As Mr D became increasingly frail he suffered from recurrent chest infections. The last was intractable and he was admitted to hospital. Mr D never recovered and he died 17 days later aged 63.

&

ELEVEN

"They were never close"

An energetic man of 72, Harold was always on the move. He could never settle. Instead, roaming around the house he would gather newspapers, magazines, letters, envelopes and paper; always paper. Once it was in his hands he seemed bemused. The task was clearly not simply to gather, but to do more. But he seemed to have little idea of what this could be. He would end up cramming it all into drawers, cupboards, under cushions or wherever he could 'file' them away. And that is what he was probably doing. He was not hiding them, for having put them away he would often take the papers out again and inspect them before starting all over again the process of tidying up and putting away.

This all drove his wife to distraction. Eunice was a woman who took particular pride in her home. She had once taken pride in her husband. A bank manager; a pillar of the local community; a director of the local rugby club. He counted a knight among his friends. For Eunice, standards were and remained very important. Unfortunately her husband now fell far short of the standards expected, and tolerant she was not. Embarrassment dominated how she felt, occasionally interspersed with resentment. She knew what was wrong with her husband – Alzheimer's disease – but that was no compensation. Every day her patience was sorely tested, for theirs was a relationship that had never been close. In many ways it had always been devoid of love and affection, and loveless marriages are not transformed into caring relationships because one of the partners has dementia.

Harold had pursued a successful career and earned a handsome salary that furnished a lifestyle both he and his wife enjoyed. Eunice, an intelligent woman, had raised their three children, created a beautiful home and there never seemed to be a local charitable, church or Women's Institute event that did not have her at the helm. Some people found her overbearing and interfering, but there was little doubt that Eunice was a woman to be respected in her own right. She was also a wonderful hostess and their dinner parties were legendary. Eunice enjoyed those evenings for this gave her the opportunity to show off their home and the trappings of their success. Now nobody was invited into her home, so ashamed was she of her husband. It was no longer 'their home' because to her Harold was now in his own world. Her home, once pristine, now felt cluttered and disorganised. It was scarred by grubby marks, discarded food and unpleasant odours.

Eunice did not neglect her husband; she just found it difficult to show tolerance and compassion. She sometimes complained to the nurses that she found him impossible.

Once she said, "I don't know whether I pity him or feel nothing for him." However, she did what she could. Constantly on the move, Horace rarely took time to eat or rest, so Eunice would prepare sandwiches and drinks for him and leave them in the kitchen. On his travels around the house he would walk through the kitchen and if he was so inclined he would have a drink or eat a sandwich more likely than not while still on the move. Hence the discarded food: crumbs throughout the house, sandwiches left half-eaten on tables and chairs, and worst of all mouldy bread and fillings found days later festering among Harold's papers having been inadvertently filed away.

What infuriated Eunice as much as her husband's roaming and incessant ramblings was his shabbiness, a further sign of standards now lost. He had once been immaculate, but no longer. For months now Harold had worn the same grimy and crumpled suit day after day. Not only would he spend his days in it, he would often sleep in it as well. She had long given up the night time struggles of trying to get him into his pyjamas. On some nights, for reasons she could never understand, Harold would of his own volition get out of his clothes, but these were rare.

The mornings were as frustrating and bizarre. Harold would welcome his wife's assistance. She would help him out of his suit and change his underwear, shirt and tie. He would mutter, "Yes, you do it." But as soon as she gave him a clean suit or a jacket and trousers to put on he would become agitated. Throwing whatever he had been given to one side and grabbing his suit he would exclaim, "No, no, never. Not can't. I tell you." If she tried to hide his suit he would become frantic and frenetically search for it.

Eventually Eunice would feel intimidated and resentful to the point where she would give in and let him get on with it. "If he wants to be a disgrace and smell to high heaven what more can I do?"

Again we heard the refrain of "that's not my husband". A man who had always been smart and immaculate had in the eyes of his wife descended into a state of wretched degradation. Eunice had embarked on numerous shopping trips to buy her husband suits, jackets, blazers and slacks that she hoped he would like. But no. The wardrobe was now full of clothes never worn and as pristine as her home had once been.

Then one morning, the weather as overcast as her mood, Eunice embarked as usual upon the daily struggle of making her husband look half decent. Why it happened Eunice has no idea but Harold surrendered the jacket of his suit. He insisted on putting the trousers back on but he accepted the sports jacket Eunice handed him from the wardrobe, one she had bought only the day before. Astounded, she seized the opportunity and threw the old jacket in the wash basket.

For months she had despaired of her husband being presentable ever again, and while the jacket and trousers did not match well at least above the waist he was well turned-out.

An hour later Eunice was beside herself with rage. She was on the telephone to the community mental health team pouring out her feelings that had been pent up for too long. No more grim determination to care, even though it had never been easy. Now she was saying what she felt. I got the full force of her anger. He had to go. There was no way she could carry on. What was the point anyhow? This wasn't the man she had married. He knew how much she had wanted him out of that disgusting suit. And what had he done? Deliberately slashed it. On purpose, to spite her. It was ruined. Why should she care about him if he felt nothing but contempt for her?

There was no placating her. So much of what she said was irrational, but this was raw emotion not considered thinking. I said we would come over straight away. I was not looking forward to the visit for I was not sure there was anything we would be able to offer Eunice. On the other hand I was intrigued. Why had Harold slashed his jacket? Since we had known him he had never been violent or destructive, and the severity of his dementia meant malicious spite was not a consideration.

I arrived with a community psychiatric nurse to find Eunice had calmed down. Having let her guard down once she was not prepared to do so again. In a matter of fact way, she described what her husband had done. How she had come across the ruined jacket discarded in the kitchen, found a pair of scissors in the sink and, lying on the kitchen table, a piece of cloth that Harold had deliberately slashed, hacked and she suspected eventually ripped off. "How could he do this to me? Does he hate me that much?" We assured her that this was not about hate, but to no effect. Emotions ruled and perspective was in hiding. Our words sounded hollow to Eunice and brought no comfort. "So why did he do it then?" she asked bitterly.

I went into the kitchen where the scissors and cloth remained. It was as Eunice described. Harold had clearly ripped the material from his jacket. Picking it up you could see that it was not only torn and frayed, but also stained. A dark tacky mark snaked down the length of the cloth. Yet this was his new jacket.

In the hall there was an occasional table. Nestling between a vase of flowers and a sculpture of a woman cradling a young child lay a half-eaten sandwich. Harold's favourite, cheese and pickle. Returning to the kitchen the stain revealed all. It was pickle. We can never be arrogant enough to say that we know what is in the mind of a person with dementia but functional analysis drives us ever closer to understanding what their intentions might be. As the psychologist Carl Rogers stated: "The best vantage point for understanding behaviour is from the internal frame of reference of the individual himself." A person with dementia will behave in a way that is appropriate in the light of how they interpret what is happening around and to them. This is the world we need to enter.

Harold had tenaciously held onto his suit and worn it day in and day out for in his mind it felt the right thing to do. Wearing a suit was what he had been accustomed to doing. Despite what was clear for all to see, the familiarity of his suit led him to feel he was dressed well. He was a man who was being true to himself, still concerned about his appearance despite all evidence to the contrary. In dementia, when a person's motivations are recognised as enduring habits that have been compromised by brain disease we talk about 'comfortable behaviour'. If they are typical of what was once appropriate but now ought to be consigned to the past, for example, behaving as if at work or bringing up children, such motivations are known as 'comfortable remnants'. A continuation of who the person has always been, or evidence of who the person once was, now manifests as a challenge to others. This clearly described the actions of Harold.

Wearing the new jacket Eunice had given him, the touch, the look, its crispness would have given Harold a sense of pride and nourished his need to be well-dressed. Then he ate the sandwich Eunice had left out for him. Eagerness, impaired eating skills, poor co-ordination, or possibly all three conspired against him. He squeezed too hard, shooting pickle down his jacket. Desperate to restore it to its previous state dementia was now to disfigure his efforts. Who has not heard the stories (possibly apocryphal) of people with dementia cutting the grass with scissors, mowing the lawn with a vacuum cleaner or placing a plastic bowl instead of a saucepan on the cooker? Harold's speech was sparse so he could not tell his wife what he had inadvertently done, apologise and ask for his jacket to be taken to the cleaners. He would have been unable to remember where to find a sponge. Maybe he did not look. His judgement was poor. Instead he picked up the scissors and proceeded to cut out the offending stain. Seeing the fruits of his labour he discarded his jacket and walked off.

I explained what I thought had happened. Eunice appreciated all I was saying but this incident was the last straw. She could not go on. She wanted her home back. She wanted to have a life again that did not involve having to think about what was she to do with Harold, a man who had become not only a source of shame, but also a burden she was unprepared to carry any longer. You see, it was not only Harold who remained the same: tragically for them both, so had their marriage. They had never been close.

TWELVE

The colour purple

This story once again concerns a striving to preserve identity. The case of Mrs D has turned out to be by no means unique but at the time I first reported her story she was the first person I had encountered whose behaviour demonstrated the enduring influence of a superstition that in Mrs D's case was grounded in religious faith.

Mrs D, a widow of 74 with probable Alzheimer's disease, lived in a local authority residential care unit for people with dementia. She had been diagnosed five years earlier, but had lived at home alone until that was no longer a realistic option. She then moved into the care home where she had been for the past month.

During the day, staff barely noticed Mrs D. She would sit in the lounge unable to say or understand much at all. She would always welcome people with a gentle smile, although it was never a sign of true acknowledgement for being severely disoriented, she knew no one. The carers described her as highly dependent but always co-operative. However, at night it was different story for Mrs D would not stay in her bedroom. The staff could predict what would happen. They would take her to her room and in the privacy of her bedroom they would get her ready for bed. This was never a challenge. Having assisted her into bed they would leave... and wait. Within minutes Mrs D would be in the corridor walking away. To where, nobody knew. To most carers she was going nowhere. It was without reason. They saw it as aimless, although possibly attention-seeking. Yet why only seek attention at night? And how could it be attention seeking when Mrs D could only remember for minutes at best? Alzheimer's disease devastates the hippocampus (the part of the brain involved in transforming experiences into learning or memory) and so now, with severe dementia, she would have been unable to appreciate the consequences of her conduct. Attention-seeking would have been beyond her.

A member of staff would accompany Mrs D back to her room. True to her pleasant self she would never resist, but once in her bedroom the difficulties truly started. She would walk out again within moments. Return her and Mrs D would immediately try to leave, and if she was prevented from doing so her behaviour would escalate. She would grimace, scream and, riding on the crest of emotion, shout out threats. "I'll hit you hard." "I'll bang it you." Occasionally, she pinched or struck out. Persist in keeping her in the bedroom and she would pull the covers off the bed, pull at the curtains, turn her bedside table over and knock over ornaments. In fact, she would try to damage or destroy all that she was physically able to do. As the weeks passed her bedroom became increasingly Spartan.

I was asked to see Mrs D because she was "unmanageable". Given she was no trouble during the day and her distressed behaviour centred on her room where she only returned at night, the logical first step was to ask why not let Mrs D leave her room and sleep elsewhere? Why not make a 'bed' in the lounge with a pillow and blankets that would allow her to sleep in an armchair? But the staff were way ahead of me. They had no problem with her sleeping in the lounge if that is what she wished to do, and on occasions they had settled Mrs D down in an armchair. However, the reality was that Mrs D was just as inclined to walk along the corridor and enter the bedrooms of other residents and get into bed alongside them. This unwelcome intrusion would not only alarm and antagonise, the ensuing commotion would upset the entire unit.

We talked about whether Mrs D was seeking companionship, but this was not the case. On occasions when a resident had been admitted to hospital, or maybe the unit was waiting for an admission, and by chance Mrs D found herself in the unoccupied bedroom, she would climb into bed and settle down. So being alone did not seem to trouble her. However, staff never left her in peace because they feared what she might do. It was one thing to trash her room, but they did not want to take the chance that she would demolish somebody else's.

It was a conundrum. Unfortunately time was not on our side as the home manager considered Mrs D to be such a threat to the welfare of the other residents she wanted immediate action. I lamely suggested placing a night light in Mrs D's bedroom in case she was agitated by a fear of the dark, but this was a gesture. I had already been told that she would settle in other bedrooms, even on those occasions when she found herself alone, and these bedrooms were equally as dark as her own, and none were particularly dark for they were all exposed to the radiant glow of the outside security lights. However, not only did the night light not work, softly illuminating her room made matters worse. For now she would no longer wait minutes to leave her bedroom but she would be found walking the corridor or entering other residents' bedrooms immediately after she had been left.

Mrs D was visited by a GP. He was told of the disruption she was causing and how this was upsetting the residents as well as exhausting the staff. He was left with little choice but to prescribe night-time sedation. However, the sedatives had no effect. The dosage was increased. This served to make her drowsy and hence more withdrawn and dependent but there was no reduction in her 'nocturnal disturbance.' With Mrs D now known as a "wanderer", "destructive" and "aggressive", the responsible social worker spoke with the psychiatrist and requested a transfer. Could Mrs D be admitted to the assessment ward to be reviewed while a man who was awaiting discharge to a dementia care unit took Mrs D's place? The psychiatrist agreed and the arrangements were put in place.

Two days before Mrs D was to be admitted to the hospital, the man fell ill with a chest infection. The exchange was put on hold until he was well enough to travel. During this hiatus a junior colleague of mine visited the care home to discuss another resident. The conversation soon drifted onto Mrs D for she was still causing havoc. My colleague, who knew nothing about Mrs D, looked at the care plan, visited her bedroom, returned to read the care plan again and then telephoned me. "I think I might know what's going on. Have you seen her room?" she queried. I had. I knew the room was the root of the problem, and it was probably something that Mrs D was seeing, which is why the night light had made matters worse, but I had to confess beyond that I was baffled.

The personal history of Mrs D in the care plan was somewhat meagre. In essence it provided the bare demographic bones of her life. She was 74, had been born in Sligo, had lived in the Midlands since the end of the Second World War, was a widow and had four children. She was also known to have worked in a launderette. In the section on 'Religion' a tick had been placed in the box adjacent to 'Roman Catholic'. As we were to find out later from one of her daughters, Mrs D had been a devout Catholic. However, as dementia took its grip she had drifted away from the church, partly, her daughter suspected, because even before the diagnosis Mrs D knew she would every so often embarrass herself. Even though he had not seen Mrs D for years, her priest confirmed the strength of her religious conviction.

The colour scheme of Mrs D's bedroom was purple and mauve. Deep purple duvet, curtains and carpet set against mauve wallpaper. In the Catholic faith the colour purple is associated with death, grief and mourning. In church at Easter, purple shrouds cover the statues and religious artefacts. Mrs D's behaviour was not without meaning, but was revealing an engrained morbid dread of the colour purple and its distressing association with death and mourning, a belief that was probably laid down in her early childhood. When away from her room she was psychologically comfortable, but when confronted with her bedroom and its colour scheme she was consumed by foreboding and sought sanctuary elsewhcre. Thus it was not where she was heading that was important, but where she was leaving. If the analysis was right, the solution lay in a simple exchange of bedrooms.

I met with a sceptical home manager who despite her reservations agreed to our suggestion that Mrs D be allocated a different room, but only after I had subjected our hypothesis to a test. I placed a cushion, one that had a pattern of yellow sunflowers on Mrs D's lap. She smiled but did nothing other than to place her hands on the cushion. Fifteen minutes later I removed the cushion and replaced it with another. This one was dark pink with a bold purple pattern. Again she smiled at me, then pushed the cushion onto the floor.

That evening Mrs D moved into a bedroom that was colour co-ordinated light and dark green and she slept throughout the night. Not once did she try to leave her room. Not on that first night or on any of the nights that followed. We had resolution. She had chosen a means to preserve her self-identity that was baffling to others and which had resulted in her being sedated at night and then referred for hospital admission. As Oliver Sacks wrote, the means chosen may be strange, or maybe it is the "disproportionate, inexplicable, unacceptable" emotional reactions when self-identity is threatened that are misunderstood. The actions chosen by people to preserve their self identity may be strange but not inevitably inexplicable, though what the person does will only make sense to others if their life history is known. For example, I have written elsewhere about Emily who had advanced dementia and lived in a care home. She would make strange, circular hand movements, bizarre and at times intimidating actions. Fortunately they were not seen by her carers as meaningless, but rightly interpreted as a "comfortable remnant" from her occupational past when she had worked in a textile mill.

The postscript to Mrs D's story occurred four days after her challenge had been resolved. The man due to be admitted to the home in her place was now well enough to be discharged from hospital. An urgent case conference was called and it was decided that Mrs D did not need to leave the home. All involved were confident, including the previously sceptical home manager, that we had achieved a lasting change in Mrs D's behaviour.

But what if that man had never fallen ill? By the time my colleague had visited the home Mrs D would already have been admitted to the assessment ward of the hospital. On her first evening the likelihood is that she would have been prescribed a major night time sedative to prevent her becoming disruptive. It would have been assumed that the medication had worked, for she would have slept soundly, but we know that would not have been the explanation. It would have been because she was away from the cause of the problem, but of course that would have remained an unknown. Or maybe Mrs D would not have slept soundly for she would now have been living her life on an open plan ward in the company of 25 people with dementia where throughout the night she would have been exposed to all sorts of noises and puzzling intrusions. Perhaps half-asleep she would have been jolted out of her slumbers by somebody, lost and bewildered staring down at her, or maybe it was Mrs D who would now be startled awake by someone climbing in to bed beside her. What a heavy price she would have paid for trying to preserve her identity.

&

THIRTEEN

"*Mum never grieved*"

S ylvia was referred because she was a risk to herself and a nuisance to others Throughout the day she would walk and walk. She was so unsteady she would stumble and fall but that did not stop her getting out of whatever chair she had decided to sit in and embarking upon her quest.

"Sylvia, do you know you fall?" I asked as I sat next to her.

"No. No, none problem... none at all... I'm fine." At which point she started to stand.

As a result Sylvia was covered in bruises. Sedation had been tried but that simply exacerbated her vulnerability as she was even more likely to fall. What was so impressive about Sylvia was her determination. She had to walk.

Staff would always keep a watchful eye but "she's slippery". At the first sign of "Sylvia's wandering again" they would rush over to support her and accompany her to the nearest chair. Unfortunately, on many occasions they were too late. Sylvia would be there one moment and gone the next, often to be found lying on the floor in a corridor or in somebody's bedroom.

What was intriguing about Sylvia's wandering was that it went beyond the normal human need to walk. To be able to walk is a fundamental human need. From only a few months old a child is on the move. Eventually we share their joy at being able to stand, followed by protective concern as they totter precariously clutching onto furniture to prevent a tumble.

Unfortunately, and too often, we are inclined to see the desire to walk in people with dementia as 'wandering', which in turn is viewed as a troublesome consequence of their condition, when there must be a distinction between the two. It has often been said that wandering is all but impossible to define because it is a term that embraces such a wide range of walking behaviour. Hence it may be the most misused label employed in dementia care. However, as the pendulum swings it is nowadays also asserted that it is a term to be avoided for, as Mary Marshall says, it may lead to care actions that fail to treat people with dementia as fellow citizens.

Yet there is good reason to distinguish between 'walking' and 'wandering' for family and professional carers know there is a distinction to be drawn between walking that is a source of pleasure and a concern to no one, and behaviour that is intrusive and drives others to despair. The challenge is to ensure that the term 'wandering' is employed in a reflective and considered fashion.

My definition of wandering is a *single-minded determination to walk that is unresponsive to persuasion, with*

> a) *no or only superficial awareness for personal safety (eg an inability to return; impaired recognition of hazard); or*
>
> b) *no apparent regard for others (e.g. in terms of time of day, duration, frequency or privacy); or*
>
> c) *no regard for personal welfare (thereby disrupting the essential behaviours of eating, sleeping, resting).*

This definition distinguishes between wandering with risk (a) and wandering as nuisance (b), as well as interpreting walking as wandering if the behaviour is 'to excess' (c) even though there is no risk or disturbance to others. The final element of the definition accommodates the finding that after entry to a safe care setting to live alongside people who are so passive and withdrawn they rarely respond, a person can sometimes be allowed to walk or pace the building hour after hour as their behaviour no longer gives rise for concern. The absence of risk or nuisance should not, however, generate complacency or inertia to the point where the pursuit of understanding is deemed unnecessary.

Without this definition walking may attract the label of 'wandering' as soon as a person with dementia walks. However, I was comfortable when staff described Sylvia's behaviour as wandering for she was determined, she could not be persuaded to sit quietly or join in an activity and she was placing herself at risk. Unlike many people who are said to be 'wanderers' yet who actually spend most of their time sitting, Sylvia was only content to sit for minutes. But why was she determined to behave this way?

Sylvia was not just at risk, but also a nuisance. She

would walk over to people, bend over and softly say, "I'm so, so sorry. Terrible, terrible," and then walk on. This would happen over and over again. Who the person was did not matter. She would walk over to anybody, sitting anywhere at any time and always say the same. "I'm so, so sorry. Terrible, terrible." It would not matter if the person glared or was abusive: she was not dissuaded from repeating her stock phrase. Nor was she trying to start a conversation for if the person replied she would ignore their words and walk away. It was sufficient for her to say what she had to and walk on. Of course, on many occasions she did not complete her quest for she would stumble.

The content of what Sylvia had to say also bore no relationship to reality for she had nothing to apologise for, nor had anything terrible happened. She was a woman with dementia living on a unit who had harmed or offended no one. The conclusion was that Sylvia's behaviour was meaningless. But if it was meaningless why was she so determined to walk when her actions placed her in such jeopardy? It was not a case of arguing that as she could not remember the damaging consequences of what she was doing she could not appreciate the risks. Her body was sore and tender. The bruises and abrasions, accompanied by grimacing, flinching and protective hand movements, were testimony to the pain Sylvia felt. Despite this she was still compelled to get out of her chair and seek out somebody to apologise to.

This all suggested that Sylvia's actions were beyond her conscious control. The explanation seemed clear: *perseveration.*

Perseveration, often referred to as the 'stuck needle syndrome', is a reason why a person with dementia may perform the same actions, say the same words, ask the same questions or walk the same route over and over again. The result of frontal lobe damage to the brain, it is involuntary behaviour that is often out of context and so has little to do with the reality of a person's situation. The person is also unable to benefit from experience even if the consequences are unpleasant or painful. Perseveration is commonly seen in fronto-temporal dementia, sometimes the result of Pick's disease (see the story of Roger in chapter 19).

Sylvia's conduct was a perfect fit except she did not have fronto-temporal dementia. Her diagnosis was probable Alzheimer's disease. This did not exclude perseveration for the spread of the disease may well have affected her pre-frontal cortex. Yet there were no other behavioural signs of frontal lobe brain damage. She was not disinhibited or impulsive, she was not apathetic or indifferent, there was no childish or silly behaviour, and nor were there any other signs of perseveration. Her wandering and need to apologise stood out as challenges in the midst of intellectual muddle, forgetfulness and dependency.

Casting doubt on whether Sylvia's behaviour was perseverative was not too dispiriting for the staff to hear, because perseveration is almost impossible to resolve. Instead you endeavour to manage the behaviour as best you can, often by using distraction to break the sequence. But if it was not perseveration that was driving Sylvia's behaviour, what else could be responsible? A conversation with her family bore rich fruit that helped us to both understand and resolve the challenge.

Twenty-seven years earlier Sylvia had lost her youngest son. He was the apple of her eye. She had been 36 when he was born, the youngest of her eight children. "Mum and Dad didn't think they'd have any more children and then Keiron was born. Mum said he was her gift from a generous Lord," one of her daughters said.

When he was just 17 years old Keiron was killed during the Troubles in Northern Ireland, an innocent lad in the wrong place at the wrong time. Sylvia was devastated, but only fleetingly. To the astonishment of her family, "Mum never grieved." Within days of her treasured son's death, Sylvia dried her eyes and became amazingly stoical, worryingly so. At the funeral she was calm and controlled, seemingly more concerned about everyone else.

As the weeks passed Sylvia acted as if nothing in her life had changed. Everyone who knew her understood something was very wrong, but Sylvia would never admit it. "I'm alright. Life has to go on," she would say. It was not that she did not appreciate what had happened; she simply did not want to talk about her son's death. Nor would she talk about Keiron. He had literally ceased to exist. Photographs of him were put away, "for safe keeping". His possessions were stored in the cellar and she never ventured into his bedroom again. She would walk out of the room if Keiron was spoken about or try to deflect the conversation onto somebody or something else. If she failed she would excuse herself. As time passed everyone knew not to talk about Keiron in front of Sylvia.

From this time on Sylvia lost her joy for life. Everybody had been taken aback by the fact that she had never grieved, but the truth was that in her own way

Sylvia had never stopped grieving. Listening to her children speak made you realize that as a mother Sylvia had been so close to her youngest child she had cherished and prized him above all others. His death tore her apart and her actions illustrated how she had been traumatised by the loss of Keiron. The shock was so great, the hurt so overwhelming the only way she could cope, you could say survive, was to repress her grief. She anaesthetised herself by repressing her heart-wrenching agony and in the process gave everyone else the impression that she was not grieving. And that is how she lived the next 25 years. Getting together with all the children happened less and less, she was rarely seen chatting with friends and neighbours and a sombre air descended on the family home. Sylvia did what she said she would, she got on with life, continued to be a doting grandmother and was always there for her children whenever they needed her, but happiness was no longer an emotion you would associate with Sylvia.

Sylvia had survived by repressing her feelings. Now she had dementia. During her waking hours the past was her companion. Present moments and recent times had never been stored, or if they had all recall had been lost. There was only the past and it was this Sylvia was destined to relive. Only a minority of people with dementia become confused in this way – actually living or reporting a reality that is different from our own – and Sylvia was one of them. She endured unremitting anguish, for all who relive their past are convinced that what they think and feel is true, real and happening at this point in time. This is their reality.

Sylvia's reality was different from our own, but it was as meaningful to her as ours is to us. Unlike Mrs O (chapter eight) and Mr D (chapter ten) memories of the past were not simply providing Sylvia with a psychological context for her actions: her memories were her life. Keiron was again in her thoughts as was the emotional trauma associated with his killing, and once again she was unable to cope. Years previously Sylvia had invoked the psychological defence of repression to contain the magnitude of her grief, and now her mind employed projection. Whereas repression excludes extreme and distressing emotions from conscious awareness, projection enables a person to cope by projecting one's own feelings and fears on to other people. So, to Sylvia, it was not she who was overwhelmed by sorrow, but others. It did not matter who, just anybody and everyone. This is why she comforted others. The intensity of the compulsion to do so reflected the depth of her own enduring hurt. Was this meaningless behaviour, or actions that could not have been more meaningful?

Sylvia's behaviour exposed the intensity of her feelings for her youngest child. Would it be possible to draw on Sylvia's love for her son and engage her in reminiscence and life-story work? Drawing on remote memories of Keiron as a child might occupy Sylvia, give her pleasure and most importantly peace of mind. With pleasurable memories absorbing Sylvia's attention, she might no longer be preoccupied with his death. In the absence of unbearable recollections there would be no intolerable upset and thus no longer any need to project her grief on to other people and be driven to console them.

It would be a risky endeavour, for reminiscing about Keiron might cue Sylvia to become even more aware of her loss and thus more agitated and desperate to defend herself, but logic is not a characteristic of confusion. A person may relive a theme of their past but still relate appropriately to aspects of the present (for example, a man with dementia may correctly recognise the woman in late middle-age as his daughter, yet will also roam the care home searching for his mother). Facts that are at odds co-exist, mingle and never undermine the reality or existence of the other. So while Sylvia knew her son was dead this did not inevitably mean that she could not also become lost in pleasurable and comforting thoughts that would be untainted by his death.

The staff did their homework. Sylvia's children told them all they could remember about their brother's life. From what they learned they compiled a life-story book. To bring it alive they asked for photos and any other memorabilia that could be pasted into the book. One of Sylvia's sisters, Mary, brought in "Keiron's stuff". When Sylvia moved into the care home her house had been sold. In the cellar they unearthed all that Sylvia had stored away in the weeks following Keiron's death.

Although it had lain untouched and unseen for decades, Mary knew that her sister would not want any of it to be thrown away, so she had taken the boxes full of football magazines, models, records, trophies won at school, his drawings, as well as his watch, and even some of his clothes including his long tartan scarf back for safe keeping, one day inevitably to be discarded. Instead they were to become a rich and intimate means of getting acquainted with Keiron. One of his brothers told us how the memories flooded back when he saw Keiron's things, memories so real "I can almost see him sitting there". If this is how he felt, what would the effect be on Sylvia?

Carers and her family would sit next to Sylvia and talk to her about Keiron as a child, at school, at home and at play, his successes, his joys and the scrapes he got himself into. All this was enriched by photos, music and the 'bits and pieces' from Keiron's life that had been hidden away for years. And it worked.

It was not so much the reminiscing of others that was uplifting, it was what she could see, touch and caress. All had been put away for safe keeping, but we know that had never really been the case. His possessions had been placed out of sight because she could not bear to be reminded of Keiron. She knew seeing them would usher in painful memories and Sylvia feared she would be unable to cope with the grief.

The memories did indeed come flooding back, but there was neither pain nor sorrow, for her memories of Keiron and the times they shared were not contaminated by desperate yearning. Instead they brought happiness. Always engrossed, she would smile and on occasions laugh. It did not matter that most of the time she was sitting alone and there was no one to reminisce with her. Simply leave Sylvia with Keiron's things and time passed without incident.

Photos absorbed her attention and she took particular delight looking at one of Keiron's sketches ("What's that, Sylvia?" – "Just a horse" she would say, and you knew from the expression on her face that it was not 'just' anything). She gained the greatest comfort from his scarf. It is this she would caress. Long, tartan and worn around the waist, as did all fans of the Bay City Rollers.

For Sylvia, her child had returned and once again she felt content, an emotion not experienced for 27 years. What irony. In the midst of dementia Sylvia had found what she must have thought was lost forever, happiness. And it would have been denied for evermore if she had not put her treasured son's possessions away – for safe keeping.

&

FOURTEEN

"She's no different from Julius Caesar"

Lucy shouted throughout the day. Incomprehensibly and inexplicably, hour after hour she would shout, ceasing only when she would fall asleep having exhausted herself. On occasions her shouting was more akin to roaring and it would echo around the building.

Lucy had been living in the home for less than a week and already there was a general feeling "How on earth are we going to cope?". The home manager was concerned not only for the welfare of the residents and care workers who were exposed to her screams and shouts hour after excruciating hour; she was also afraid that a resident would be pushed too far by Lucy's incessant noise and she would be assaulted. Already some were shouting out in response, "We don't want her in here." Her behaviour corresponded with my definition of what constitutes a challenging behaviour: *an act of severity, as measured by intensity, frequency or duration, that places the physical safety or psychological health of the person or others at risk.*

149

The manager had every reason to be concerned. Lucy not only had advanced dementia, she was also frail. Every morning she would be transferred from a wheelchair and sat in the lounge. Unable to care for herself she was placed with the other highly dependent residents in a light and airy part of the lounge facing a large panoramic window. The chairs had been arranged in crescents for this provided a pleasant outlook onto the garden. Admirably, the staff were determined that even their most dependent residents would have a quality of life even though frailty meant that most would spend their days sitting in the lounge doing little. Providing a pleasant view was a start.

Knowing the situation was fast becoming intolerable the manager telephoned the GP. The GP enquired whether Lucy was one of her residents with dementia. Given all the home's residents were she said "yes, of course," wondering why the doctor had even asked. Then it became clear. She was told that if she or one of her staff waited until the end of surgery they could come down and pick up a prescription. The pathology-centred approach to understanding dementia was again over-reaching itself, but the home manager had not telephoned in the hope that the doctor would agree to sedate Lucy. She knew her residents were people with needs and ways that were unique to them, but she also appreciated they had needs that we all share – one of which is to be free of pain. This is why she had contacted the GP.

Pain is one of the most obvious reasons why a person with dementia might shout or call out, often unintelligibly. All people with severe dementia are affected by a devastating loss of language and so a question when caring for people at this point on the spectrum of dependency is: how are they able to communicate discomfort, soreness or unpleasant clinical sensations in a way that those who are caring can readily understand? Could this be why Lucy was yelling? However, the doctor's question implied a belief that in some way Alzheimer's disease exercises miraculous protection from illness and pain. Lucy was in her eighties, an age when chronic pain and discomfort becomes frequent. Yet this did not prompt the GP to think that maybe his patient was in pain, and that it was Lucy his patient who, in her fragile and distressed state, needed to be his principal concern. While understandably wishing to be of assistance, the GP's primary responsibility was not to help the care home by exorcising their difficulty.

The manager had hoped that the doctor would visit in order to examine Lucy and possibly review her medication, but given this was clearly not going to happen, she thanked the GP for his suggestion but declined his offer and said they would endeavour to manage as well as they could.

Reflecting on Lucy's behaviour, the manager realised it was unlikely to be pain, for Lucy only shouted in the lounge. She never made a noise in her bedroom, when in the toilet, nor when being taken in a wheelchair along the corridors. During the first two days at the home they had helped Lucy adjust to her new surroundings by letting her stay in her room and not once did she shout out. It was only when she started spending her days in the lounge that the screaming started.

The explanation was clear. She was frightened or

annoyed by the other residents. It was how it must have been for Janet (see chapter six) as she struggled to survive on the hospital ward in the midst of people who were not only menacing and strange, but whose behaviour did not follow the rules of social conduct.

Could it be fear that was motivating Lucy to shout? This is another common explanation and one that corresponded with Lucy's pattern of behaviour. If yes, the solution was obvious. Lucy needed to sit away from other residents. No one thought it was a good idea for her to stay in her bedroom for it was not particularly large and was also somewhat sparse. So the decision was taken for her to sit in the corridor in splendid isolation. I do not want to give the impression that this was akin to a punishment. Lucy was seated in a nook by a staircase next to a window where the sun shone through in the morning. Quite a pleasant spot, where staff placed an armchair and occasional table, and there Lucy sat and not a sound was heard. However, in order to resolve the challenge they had been forced to exclude Lucy from the lounge and any social opportunities that might have come her way. This is why the full definition of challenging behaviour includes the following concluding statement:

... or limits the person's access to normal lifestyle opportunities thereby resulting in social exclusion.

For nine weeks the revised care plan worked without a hitch. Not once was Lucy heard shouting. Away from people with dementia she appeared comfortable and at peace. For nine weeks relative calm and tranquillity reigned, and then... I do not know whose fault it was. Did the manager forget to tell the new care assistant that she must read Lucy's care plan or was she told but forgot to do so? Whatever the explanation, Lucy was destined not to sit in the place that had become her haven. The care assistant got Lucy out of bed and helped her to wash and dress. As you might expect Lucy's breakfast was brought to her room where the care assistant helped her to eat. Now ready for the day ahead, Lucy was taken out of her room and because she knew no different the care assistant headed toward the lounge.

Lucy was taken over to where the highly dependent residents sat and transferred to an armchair. Within minutes Lucy was screaming out at the top of her voice. Of course she was. She had to be separated from the other residents. They bothered her. Possibly they startled her, and that is why the care plan stated she was not to be seated in the lounge. The only problem was that on this occasion there was nobody else in the lounge. Shouting even though she was alone – how could this be?

Lucy could not recall what was happening in her life from one moment to the next and so there was no way that she could have remembered the circumstances of her life from weeks earlier. She could not have thought, 'there's nobody with me at the moment, but anytime soon that's going to change' and hence she was protesting in anticipation.

To the surprise of everybody the reason for Lucy's behaviour clearly lay elsewhere. We talked through the success of the revised care plan which had demonstrated how she had benefited from no longer sitting with other residents. But had it? Had Lucy been socially excluded unnecessarily?

As Lucy's story unfolded I was curious about why the fact that she had only created a noise in the lounge had not undermined the explanation the care team had reached. Why had Lucy never shouted in the dining room? After those first two days when care had been centred on her room, Lucy had been taken with the other residents to have her lunch in the communal dining room. Sat at a table with three other people, all of whom had eating and swallowing difficulties, she was helped to eat her meal. Despite sitting at the table for nearly an hour she never showed any signs of complaint or distress.

Why had this not informed the analysis? In a way it had: although never entered in the care plan, it had been thought that she would have been reassured by the close support of carers who would have been assisting her, as well as being distracted by the mealtime activity. While this reasoning could not be automatically discounted, it was unlikely. There would have been times when carers would not have been in close proximity and there would have been time spent just waiting – for her meal, to be assisted or before being taken back to the lounge. Periods of time when Lucy would have had little to either preoccupy or distract her – but not once had she been heard to shout out.

The experience in the dining-room and now the knowledge that Lucy had screamed in the lounge when there was nobody else present suggested that it was not people she was disturbed by, but the lounge. She could not be calling out in discomfort for the chairs in the lounge were the same as the armchair she sat in for hours in the nook by the staircase. There was nothing about the atmosphere in the lounge that would have disturbed her. There were no unpleasant aromas, the lights did not glare and there was no constant grating background noise from a television or CD player.

This left just one avenue to investigate. Could Lucy be seeing something that was alarming her? What was in her line of vision? The garden view was pleasant but unremarkable: swaying branches of a laburnum tree, flower beds typical of a cottage garden – towering red hot pokers, hollyhocks, delphiniums, irises and lupins – and a rolling lawn. Lucy was passive and rarely turned to gaze elsewhere. I sat in each of the chairs that looked onto the garden, and that's all there was to see. I was sitting in an armchair gazing past a china cat lazing on the window sill, admiring a garden bursting with colour. And there it was, the reason for Lucy's distress.

Ailurophobia is an abnormal and persistent fear of cats. Sufferers fear not only the scratch or bite of a cat, but also the 'evil mystique' of cats as depicted in Halloween folklore and elsewhere. It has been known for people with ailurophobia not only to become anxious but to break out in a sweat at the sight of a cat, have difficulty breathing and even become hysterical.

While ailurophobia is not that uncommon, most people like cats, some even adore them, and those who cannot tolerate even being near to cats do not talk about it that much. So how were the staff to suspect, let alone know, that the black and white china cat was to Lucy not an ornament to admire or ignore, but instead (probably misinterpreting it as a real cat) was a source of terror? "She's no different from Julius Caesar or even Napoleon," I cryptically said. I could have said Genghis Khan, Mussolini and Hitler, for all these tyrants from the past are reputed to have suffered from a fear of cats.

The 'cat' was removed and the response was immediate – blissful lasting silence.

The figurine is now to be found gracing a window sill elsewhere in the home and Lucy sits in the lounge, looks out onto the garden and not a sound is heard. Sometimes it is the obscure we need to seek out rather than being constrained by concentrating on the obvious. If we are watchful and creative in our thinking we can brainstorm possible explanations for any behaviour that challenges us . The process may lack scientific rigour, but it brings a dynamic approach to enquiry. We do not know that our understanding was correct, for there was nobody left in Lucy's life to tell us, but the removal of the figurine worked and in the final analysis that is all that matters. Of course, it is possible that she may have been fearful of china cats, but somehow I doubt it.

&

PART III

The good, the bad and the indifferent

"We have, each of us, a life-story... whose continuity, whose sense, is our lives."
– OLIVER SACKS

FIFTEEN

Indignity upon indignity

Patrick was referred to me because he was "deliberately incontinent", which is clearly a contradiction in terms: a person cannot be deliberately incontinent. Incontinence is not a description of someone who wets or soils themselves; it is a possible reason why they might do so. To say somebody is incontinent is to know they have lost or damaged bladder or bowel control. Until a person reaches the later stages of dementia, most are as continent as those who care for them (except in cases of fronto-temporal dementia when it can be an early symptom). Yes, they may wet and soil themselves but this is more likely to be because they cannot find the toilet, have not got the dexterity to open doors, are feeling depressed and 'can't be bothered', cannot undo their clothing or a myriad of other explanations that have nothing to do with incontinence.

Staff were using the term 'incontinence' to wrongly label Patrick. They knew he retained bladder control for they saw his actions as being deliberately manipulative. "He's an attention-seeker," one said. Another saw him as a "dirty old man" for she believed he simply enjoyed being intimately cared for by the female carers. His sons, who visited regularly, were beside themselves. A mixture of sadness, disgust and loathing summed up their feelings. They would say, "Our father was such a proud and dignified man. He never would have degraded himself in this way... Sometimes it's hard to still see him as our father."

Because the carers knew something about Patrick they thought they were working in a 'person-centred' way. He had been born in Omagh in Northern Ireland, but he had lived in Liverpool most of his adult life where he had worked as a postman. He had six children, four of whom were sons, and he had been widowed eight years ago. That was it. An effort had been made but they had hardly scratched the biographic surface let alone shown any real interest in Patrick the man. There had been no attempt to unearth his likes and dislikes, interests and favoured activities, routines and habits, let alone his fears, insecurities and superstitions. Their failure was compounded by a complete lack of regard for the subjective experience of dementia. No-one had contemplated what it must be like for Patrick to be in a world he struggled to comprehend.

Everything the staff told me about Patrick's behaviour was true and accurate. He would be taken to the toilet and refuse to use it. They were patient and gave him time, but to no avail. Eventually, he would be accompanied back to the lounge and then he would be found wet, having deliberately soiled himself even though he had been given every opportunity to use the toilet just minutes earlier. "He can be a swine. Never nasty, but..."

While that is how it was in reality, it must have felt very different to Patrick. He had recently been assessed using the Mini Mental State Examination (MMSE) – a commonly-used set of questions and exercises to test memory and intellect – and had scored 11/30. In the care plan "moderate to severe dementia" had been written. Patrick was also unsteady on his feet. Unsurprisingly, he spent most of his day sitting in the lounge. On occasions he would venture out of his chair and he would be seen walking around the building, frequently pausing to hold onto a handrail, sometimes to catch his breath. Patrick would be returned to a chair.

If his walking suggested he might be searching for a toilet he was likely to be unsuccessful. The care home was not legible to him: in other words it was disorienting and made little sense. Seeing dementia as a disability helps us realise that the care environment – both buildings and relationships – can either support and possibly compensate for weaknesses, or actively disable a person.

Buildings should not rely on the person with dementia having a memory of where they are, how they got there and where to go. However, in this care home that is exactly how it was. Visual access helps to compensate for the inability to remember but in this care home visual access was poor. If the goal is in a person's line of vision, a thought, such as "I want the toilet" or a suggestion "Do you think it might be a good time for you to go to the toilet?" is maintained not because it is remembered, but because the goal is never out of sight. It acts as a recurring cue pulling the person to their destination. In this way the environment is legible, but this was not the case where Patrick lived. The toilets were out of sight, tucked away along corridors and to make matters worse the building was anonymous. Nearly every door was identical. There was no signposting or cueing to compensate for the residents' inability to find their way around, and so it was little wonder that many of the residents were said to be 'incontinent'!

Being both unable to find his way around, and unsteady on his feet, Patrick always needed to be taken to the toilet. Every three hours he would be accompanied there by two carers, typically two women. He would be taken into the toilet, his clothing lowered and, having sat him on the toilet they would step back and hover about two feet away, invariably having a chat. That proud and dignified man as described by his sons must have been mortified. So embarrassed, he either could not or would not use the toilet. And this is where dementia stepped in.

I often feel that a useful way of understanding dementia is to see it as a barrier. A person disabled by cognitive losses on one side, and us on the other side, both unable to understand each other or take each others' perspective; or maybe in our case it can often be less to do with inability and more to do with too many of us being unprepared to do so.

Patrick could say little and hence he was unable to articulate how he must have felt: "What do you think you're doing? Could you please step outside and give me some privacy?" Nor could he remember that this happened every three hours and that if he did not use the toilet he was going to have problems soon after. Nor could he reason "they must have done a risk assessment and they believe I'm going to topple off onto the floor, and so they are here to catch me". Dementia had devastated his language, memory and reasoning, but it had not destroyed him. With him sitting there immobile, doing nothing, the carers despaired of him. Sometimes they would coax him, but most often having given him a few minutes they would take him off the toilet, rearrange his clothes and lead him away.

But what had they done? They had cued him into the fact that he needed the toilet. Minutes after having been left in the lounge, Patrick was compelled to wet himself, and misunderstanding would escalate. He was seen as wilfully incontinent; no one appreciated his plight. Looking at the experience through Patrick's eyes he had responded if not appropriately, at least understandably. As has been said "abnormal behaviour in an abnormal situation is normal behaviour". He had done his best, but that could not prevent a personal tragedy unfolding, for his efforts to preserve his dignity always led to the indignity of soiling himself and then having to be changed.

Speaking to the staff it was easy to reveal that they had not truly been working in a person-centred way. Their preoccupation with dementia and the tasks of caring was so much to the fore that Patrick, the man, lagged so far behind as to hardly matter. Staff also had a disproportionate sense of risk. Limitations were placed on residents' movements and privacy was invaded all in the name of risk management. I said, "There's no need to talk to me about Patrick's dementia. Everybody here has dementia, so let's not dwell on what we know already. Let's put dementia on the back burner and bring Patrick as a person to the fore. Can you imagine how humiliating it must be for him to see you standing there waiting for him to perform? You don't do that to people."

As for risk, there may be a need for a discreet presence, but that only follows a risk assessment. It is a falsehood to believe that people with dementia inevitably propel themselves off toilet seats if they are left alone. Throughout the day people with dementia sit in chairs unaided, unsupported and unobserved with no hint of concern from those who care for them but as soon as they are placed on toilet seats we find doors left open and carers standing by or over them 'just in case'. Too often these are disproportionate and degrading actions.

Patrick's competence in the toilet had never been risk assessed. Assessment revealed that while he could not walk far without losing balance, sitting unsupervised on a toilet seat was not a hazard. With Patrick, the person, no longer hidden behind a diagnosis of dementia and carers now holding an enlightened appreciation of risk, Patrick was taken to the toilet, assisted with his clothing, helped to sit down and then... left alone. Standing outside, care staff would close the door and wait. After a few minutes they would knock on the door and enter. On 80% of occasions Patrick had used the toilet and from this time on he rarely wet or soiled himself.

Had there been a miraculous cure of his dementia? Of course not. Had an unthinking, unsupportive and insensitive care environment been exposed and resolved? Yes, and it was dehumanising treatment, unseen by the staff who cared for him, that had been responsible for the degradation of Patrick, not his dementia. However, it was not only the carers who were blind to what was happening. When the GP had last visited, the staff's complaints had reached such a pitch that he said that if Patrick's incontinence could not be controlled he would come again with the continence nurse and catheterize him.

&

SIXTEEN

A devoted father

David and his family were facing an extraordinary tragedy. Only 49 years of age and he had probable Alzheimer's disease. Eighteen months ago he had been a fairly successful car dealer. "Nearly new cars," he would say, correcting my description of his occupation as a "second hand car dealer". Only reasonably successful, for in recent times the business had not done well. Sales down, deals lost, poor decisions taken. The reason why was now clear, but at the time his wife had been mystified.

Having been referred by his GP, David's brain scan had revealed marked brain atrophy (the loss of brain cells and the connections between them). All of his symptoms, the progression of his intellectual decline and his presentation in interview cried out "Alzheimer's disease". It was decided to enter David into a drug trial that was examining the benefits of donepezil, one of the new 'anti-dementia drugs'. We explained that it might slow down

David's dementia, but as it was a trial there was a chance he could be prescribed a placebo, although maybe for only part of the trial. David agreed, but as his judgement was poor, his wife was consulted and she too agreed.

David entered the trial and life continued. His wife coped with her husband's decline by going out to work every morning. This helped by allowing her to put both emotional and physical distance between herself and, if not her husband, then her worries for the future: "Sometimes I think I'm selfish, but at work I switch into work mode, and for hours on end I forget what's happening to us. I need that. I couldn't cope if I couldn't switch off." She was a successful computer analyst, and now held a senior manager's position. Every morning she would commute into the city centre knowing all would be well at home.

Before leaving she would make David sandwiches and a salad, and make up a flask of coffee for him. She would make sure the television was on ("He can still use the remote control, but I can't trust him to make a cup of coffee. That's a man for you!") and off she would go knowing all day he would stay in the house watching television. Channel hopping, more accurately, for David's concentration was too poor to follow a programme. But channel hopping had its attractions and he was content. There was also the alarm clock to set. This was critical. Set the alarm for 3.25pm and place the clock on the mantelpiece.

David did next to nothing all day. He had settled into a sedentary lifestyle remarkably quickly, but at 3.25 there was something he had to do and he never forgot. Yes, he had to be prompted by the alarm, but thereafter you could set your clock by him.

David and Amanda had two young children. Amanda wanted a career so they had left it somewhat late to start a family. She told us that from the moment Alex was born David had relished being a father. Devoted and attentive, he would do anything for his children. Sometimes Amanda felt that David was the more natural parent, and for this she was grateful for she was committed to her career. For David his job was simply a means of earning money.

Alex was now 11 years old and had just started secondary school, but Alice who was only eight was at primary school and needed to be picked up at the end of the day. Without fail that is what David did. The alarm would sound and David would leave the house. He would walk down the road, turn left at the junction and walk to the end of the cul-de-sac where his daughter would soon be running through the playground to the school gate. Together they would return hand-in-hand. It was touching to see and he never let her down. Dementia was not going to stop him being a dutiful father.

That is how life was during the year I knew David. I was monitoring his response to treatment every four weeks. After 12 months a decision had to be taken. Should David stay on the drug treatment, or were there reasons to leave the trial? I made an error of judgement.

I had been monitoring David's rate of decline. This included repeat administration of the Mini Mental State Examination (MMSE). Even though the rate of cognitive decline is highly variable among people with Alzheimer's disease you can estimate that the natural evolution of mild dementia will result in the loss of 3-5 points on the MMSE each year. David's results showed that not only had there been no evidence of stability, but his score had declined from 23/30 to 17/30. As this suggested normal progression I concluded David had been on a placebo drug, which is why we had seen no positive effects. In daily life Amanda told me that David was not the same as a year ago. He was less talkative, more easily distracted and definitely more absent-minded. On occasions she had found herself wondering whether she had better make alternative arrangements to ensure their daughter arrived home safely from school, but every afternoon David was there at the school gate waiting for Alice. She decided to leave well alone.

What to do? At the time he entered the drug trial Amanda had told me that her husband might not stay on it for long because he had never liked doctors and so he would not enjoy my visits. More significantly he had never liked taking tablets, so he might not comply with the treatment regime. As it turned out there were few problems, although on occasions David had to be persuaded to take the medication he had been prescribed. While David participated and more often than not complied willingly, I now reflected on what I had been told. If David was on a placebo and he was a man who was uncomfortable with doctors and taking tablets, why persist with the trial? I talked over the decision to be taken with colleagues and we recommended to Amanda that David could now leave the trial. She agreed and at the end of the week David took his last placebo pill – except it was not. Within a fortnight David's MMSE score had plummeted to 7/30. The Drug Trials Unit confirmed David had been on an active treatment throughout the trial and what the donepezil had been doing was holding at bay a particularly aggressive dementia. The rate of decline I had observed was 'normal', but David's dementia was not. Arrangements were made for him to go back onto donepezil and his MMSE score rebounded to 14/30, but the damage had been done. David was not restored to his previous self. He was more muddled, prone to doing silly careless things and more dependent.

Amanda tried to keep family life on an even keel and as normal as she could. Well, as normal as dementia will allow. She went to work, the children got themselves ready for school and David would still sit in the chair all day with the television on, although now the remote control was beyond him. In part because she could not rely on David anymore, partly because their daughter was embarrassed and to a certain extent because it was not too inconvenient, Alice now stayed back at school for 20 minutes so she could walk home with her brother.

One day a few weeks later, Amanda's world collapsed. Alice was on the telephone sobbing as she tried to explain what was happening. They had come home from school and had found dad in the toilet, sitting on the seat sideways on with his trousers and pants around his ankles, and with his knees wedged against the wall. There was toilet paper all over the place and he had got himself into a mess. Alex had tried to help his dad but it had degenerated into a bit of a struggle. Alex, feeling awkward and out of his depth, and David, embarrassed and not fully understanding what was going on were caught up in the confusion of the moment. Alex frantically yelled out to his sister, "Telephone mum!"

Enough was enough. Amanda had tried to carry on, but no more. It was not simply that she could no longer leave in the morning and lose herself in work knowing all was well at home. She was worried what effect this was having on Alex and Alice. Until now they had both been marvellous. They could see the changes in their father but they seemed to have taken it all in their stride. They understood that he was ill and that sometimes he might forget, do silly things and on some days might need a bit of help in whatever he might be trying to do, but he was still their father who loved them greatly. In the evening Alice would often sit on the settee with David and watch television with him as he stroked her hair, something he had done since she was tiny. They had always been close. You could see they had a special relationship and for them the day still started as it always had done, having breakfast together, chatting while they ate and squabbling about who should wash up and who should put away. Life for the two of them often appeared little different.

Nowadays, it had all changed. Alice was not sleeping, Alex had become angry with his dad and Amanda had been given compassionate leave in order to care for David while we arranged an emergency care plan. Within days the social worker had arranged for David to enter a nursing home for a period of respite care. He entered the home one Sunday afternoon inarticulate and disoriented, and on the first two mornings he hit the nurses who were helping him out of bed. Later on the evening of the third day having become 'difficult' David hit the on-call GP. Immediately an emergency admission was requested. Two hours later David was on the acute admission ward "for assessment and management of his unprovoked violence". He was never to be violent again.

The nurses on the ward thrived within a culture of what is called 'Gentlecare'. Supportive, tolerant and empathic person-centred care governed all they did. There was a minimum of fuss and routine. Very different from where David had just spent the best part of three days. We had known that care within this nursing home was dominated by 'must', 'got' and 'have to' (known as 'the tyranny of the should' wherein routines masquerade as rules to be slavishly followed), but because Amanda and the children could no longer cope we had not had the luxury that time affords to delay admission until a vacancy arose in a more acceptable care home. The home demonstrated a style of care that Tom Kitwood referred to as the "taken-for-granted world of later life" when he introduced the term 'malignant social psychology' into our understanding of dementia care (see chapter two).

Not knowing where he was, not knowing who people were, what sense could David make of people coming into his bedroom, throwing back the covers and telling him it was time to get up? And why did the staff feel the need to act in this way? Did he have an appointment to keep; a bus to catch; a visitor to greet? No. Was something going to happen in the lounge and he would be so disappointed if was to arrive late and found he had missed out? No. He had to get up now, because now was the time to get up! Breakfast would be served within the hour and everybody had to be seated in the dining-room waiting. But why did David have to get out of bed right away? Why not in ten minutes, 20 minutes, or why could he not stay in bed, have a lazy morning and have a bowl of cereal, a couple of slices of toast or a cereal bar later in the morning? No, the home ran according to strict routines in order that it could run smoothly (what Koch and Webb referred to as 'conveyor belt care').

We had regularly been asked in the past to advise on "uncooperative residents" there, but when that request happens with ceaseless regularity you know this is less to do with the residents, and more to do with a home that is dominated by inflexible routines. For what does uncooperative mean? It means the person will not do what they are told to do at the very moment they are told to do it! And if they persist in their awkward ways they are likely to be labelled as aggressive. With David, little time had to pass before he was considered not just 'aggressive' but 'violent'. Startled and unknowing, offended by the nurses' intrusive behaviour, he had lashed out – and of course he had never liked doctors. In this instance the doctor had been trying to calm him by giving him an injection of the tranquilliser diazepam.

On the hospital ward life could not have been more different. Having knocked on his bedroom door the nurse would partially open the curtains and gently rouse David. She would orientate him by telling him where he was, who she was and why she was in his room. "Would you like to get up or how about if I come back in a few minutes? Why not have a doze and I'll come back shortly. Shall I turn your radio on?" And off she would go. Returning minutes later, she would open the curtains and repeat the information already given. "Would you like to get up now, or I know, why don't I first get you a cup of tea?" David would be left for ten minutes or so with his tea. Now awake, unrushed and unthreatened, David was more than happy to get out of bed – but if he did not want to, so be it. Routines were kept to a minimum. As life unfolded in similar vein, on no occasion was David abusive or resistive, let alone violent.

However, this was an assessment ward and the number of beds on this specialist unit, staffed by expert nurses of the highest calibre, were few in number. This was not a place where people came to live. As two weeks became three, we had to think of the future. Where was David going to live? In the ward review Amanda said she could not have David back home again. While his violent behaviour had been an aberration he was very dependent. Who would care for him while she was at work and what effect would having their father back home have on Alex and Alice? No, it was impossible to even contemplate.

David joined the meeting and as the decision to be reached was explained to him Amanda dissolved into tears. She knew that David would want to come home. He had no idea how dependent he was. He would want to be with his family and the image of him sitting with Alice every morning having breakfast chatting and joking about the day ahead would not go away. Instinctively David reached over to comfort Amanda. This caused the tears to flow even more. David looked bemused. He was told that it was time for him to leave the hospital.

"No. I don't. No," he said, almost apologetically.

"David, you can't live here," somebody said.

He looked at Amanda. She said nothing.

"...and it's not a good idea for you to go back home. We would like you to think about living somewhere else?"

"Stop it!" Amanda exclaimed, "Can't you see David doesn't know what to do. He can't know. He has no idea what's going on."

As everybody in the room looked awkward, David started to say over and over again, "Not home, no there again, 'nother place. No there again, 'nother place."

Little insight, unable to reason – with an MMSE score still hovering around 14 it was understandable that we had assumed this was so. However, here was David struggling with his words but communicating self-awareness and rational thought. We were taken aback because here was a man with serious dementia telling us that he understood he could not return home. He knew his family was suffering, but equally he did not want to go back to the care home that weeks earlier had made his life intolerable. Somewhere else, another place would do. Residual memory traces, an element of comprehension and a vestige of reasoning enabled him to remain a man who was helping us to make the right decision.

As the meeting progressed and the minutes passed, David became increasingly agitated. The numbers of people present, the questions, the discussion were all too much. Soon he was happy to leave the room and sit in the adjacent lounge. When the nurse who accompanied him returned she told us that as they walked down the corridor David kept muttering, "Knew I could do it.

Knew I could do it." Even as he embarked on the next stage of his journey, more deteriorated than ever, he was still not going to let his daughter down.

This time we were not going to be rushed into a hasty decision. David had told us what he was prepared to accept and he was not going to be failed again. Special provision was made and he stayed on the ward for nearly nine weeks until he was found a place in a nursing home that had an excellent reputation for considerate and sensitive care embodied in a compassionate manager whose enthusiasm shone like a beacon. In the home Amanda and the children were made to feel welcome and during their regular visits family life was resurrected. And that is how it remained for the rest of David's life. To this day I am convinced that David's words in the case review nourished the love Amanda felt for her husband, and as the years passed and the children understood better what had happened, I feel their love for their father also deepened. If David had known, this devoted father would have been happy.

&

SEVENTEEN

"It's a pity you can't be here more often"

Peter lived in a nursing home and he continued to be as violent as the day he arrived. Married to him for 18 years, violence was the reason why Mary had been unable to cope. "I know I've failed him, but I couldn't carry on." She had taken his muddled thinking, the repetitive questions and the fact that he could never be left on his own in her stride, but the unrestrained assaults were another matter. On the day his wife accompanied him to the care home she had shown the nurses the bruises on her arms and shoulders. Mary told them that time and time again she had shouted at him, "You're hurting me. Please stop." But he never did. Even the sight of his wife in pain failed to bring the violence to an end. He would bend her fingers back, punch, pinch and pull her hair. "Do you know there were occasions when I could see in his eyes that he wanted to hurt me."

Peter's violence had never been unpredictable, and so it remained in the nursing home. He would lash out during any form of intimate personal care. Washing, bathing, dressing, undressing and helping him in the toilet would always incur his wrath, and it was this inevitability that had made caring so difficult for Mary. She always knew what was to come and unless she was going to neglect her husband she literally knew how painful the day would be. Now the same foreboding gripped many of the nurses who cared for him.

There was no reasoning with Peter. Carol, the senior nurse, who is one of the most committed and creative nurses I have had the privilege to work with, had reluctantly conceded that a major tranquilizer, Quetiapine, was the only way to calm Peter. Unfortunately, he had reacted poorly to the medication and it was discontinued. The nurses were again exposed to the full extent of Peter's ferocity.

Why was this once successful solicitor, who according to his wife had no shred of malice within him, acting so violently whenever there was a need for intimate personal care? As I got to know them both I learnt that Peter, a handsome and imposing man, had always been competitive in all that he did, but at the same time (and somewhat paradoxically) he was also reserved and mild –mannered. It appeared that at the core of this man had been a steely determination to succeed. It would have surprised many, for what they would have invariably seen would have been the refined and attractive 'velvet glove'.

Mary admitted that there was much she did not know about her husband. For both of them it was their second marriage. They met at a party having been introduced by a mutual friend. Eight months later they married. They were both in their late forties. Mary quickly learnt she had to adjust to Peter's ways. She told me that he was an intensely private man who was uncomfortable with intimacy. Mary disclosed that she had never seen him naked and that lovemaking had always been under the cover of darkness. Peter loved his sport and had played a lot of tennis and cricket, but he would never take a communal shower. He would always wait until he returned home. I doubt whether anybody ever enquired why, because Peter was not the sort of man you would question. His charming, aristocratic bearing would have ensured that everyone accepted him for who he was.

Mary was aware that if the subject of his childhood came up, Peter would either have good reason to be elsewhere or he would silently disappear behind a newspaper. In the early years she had asked on many occasions why intimacy was so difficult for him, but such was his discomfort that the conversations would eventually peter out and she was left none the wiser.

On one occasion Peter seemed to be opening up, and just for a few moments he had let his guard slip. She could not be sure, but from that day on Mary always believed that something had happened to him when he was evacuated as a boy during the Second World War. In all likelihood he had been abused. It was conjecture, but for Mary it was enough for her never to feel the need to ask again.

If Peter had been abused as a child, this offered an explanation for his unwillingness to expose himself to others, his avoidance of intimacy and, now suffering from dementia, his aversion to intimate care. Curiously, while he ferociously resisted care at the hands of the nurses this was no longer the case with Mary. If Mary was present not only would he visibly calm down, he was far more inclined to let her do what he would not let the nurses do, even though his violent resistance to being cared for by Mary was the reason why he had come into the care home. We never were able to work out why Peter was now more accepting of Mary's assistance – we were just grateful that he was. Unfortunately, one day a well-meaning nurse happened to say to Mary after her arrival had again calmed Peter down "It's a pity you can't be here more often". Yes, her presence did work wonders, but it was not the most tactful comment to have made.

Mary took the nurse's words as implied criticism. She spoke with Carol and explained that she could not visit more often. She was already coming three or four times a week. She now had a part-time job, as well as looking after her daughter's two children every day after school. There was no way she could do any more. Carol assured Mary that there had never been any intention to imply criticism. In fact, what the nurse had said should be seen as a compliment.

When I found out what had happened, a germ of an idea started to grow in my mind. Mary's visits were a great benefit not only to the hard-pressed staff but importantly they helped Peter. Nobody wants to be hit, but equally no one wanted to see Peter agitated and angered to the point where he was driven to violence. From what we were seeing it was quite likely that if Mary could be around more often her husband would be comforted by her presence. While practically this was not possible, would it be possible to conjure up her being there?

Simulated presence therapy was first described in a paper by Woods and Ashley. They reported how playing an audio-tape of a husband or wife's voice simulates their presence and by making the person feel more secure it serves to calm and soothe, and may even alleviate aggression and agitation in dementia. In the few studies that have been published it was clear that simulation presence therapy does not work for all people – but might it help Peter?

I met with Mary and reiterated that the nurse's comment was a compliment. Clumsy, but a compliment nevertheless, and in many ways the nurse was right. Peter was calmer and happier during her visits. In turn Mary reiterated that it was impossible for her to visit more often. As she began to say she would try to lengthen the duration of her visits I stopped her and said, "What if we were to pretend you were here?"

"What, like having a cardboard cut out of me standing in the corner?"

"Funnily enough that's not a million miles from what I'm about to suggest."

And so our simulation presence therapy project commenced. I asked Mary if she could select two or three photos of her and Peter – if she did not mind the assault on her vanity, the more historical the better. We would then get them enlarged to poster size. That was the easy part. We then had to overcome her reticence. For when I asked whether she would record an audio-tape for us, she declined. She said she would feel too self-conscious. I explained that we did not want a monologue but for her to sit quietly for 15 minutes, relax, let the tape run and when the moment felt right start to reminisce about the good times she and Peter had shared, the special events, even the funny moments. I said that if she felt able to do so, it would do no harm if she could weave into the nostalgia statements such as "I'll be coming to see you soon" or "let the nurses help you". As we talked her face wore a look of sadness. "I owe Peter so much. What's happened to him is awful," she said in a flat, cheerless tone. "Let's give it a try."

Mary did all we asked. We had three photographs to display, one of their wedding day, one of Mary resplendent on Lady's Day at Ascot and one of them in their garden sitting under the wisteria. The tape was a testimony to their loving marriage and touching to hear.

Peter's violence was specific to his personal care and always predictable. From now on, whenever staff got Peter ready for the day or helped prepare him for bed at night the posters were displayed in his room. Before attempting any care task, the nurses would tell him that Mary had sent a message and they were going to play it for him. It was difficult to know how much Peter understood but we did not want a disembodied voice appearing in the room which could have disconcerted him and caused Peter to be even more aggressive. A nurse would start the tape and then throughout the time they spent with him they would make reference to what Mary was saying and talk to him about Mary using the photographs as cues and topics of conversation.

Simulated presence therapy had an immediate effect. Despite the intimate nature of the care tasks Peter was visibly calmed. He was never completely at ease, but he was less resistive, more cooperative and on occasions he would even smile. As the weeks and months passed there was no doubt that the therapy was working. At times the tape would dominate, at other times the nurses would talk more. All the time the objective was to introduce and maintain a sense of Mary in the room. Occasionally Peter would flare but the incidents of violence were dramatically reduced.

What were the therapeutic ingredients? I do not believe that Peter understood much that was said to him, so I doubt whether it was Mary's reminiscences that calmed him, but hearing Mary's voice as well as seeing familiar and favourite photographs must have invoked a sense of her presence. That is what simulated presence therapy is meant to do, but could it be that Peter was distracted by the nurses talking to him, and that the set-up did not have to simulate Mary's presence in order to work? Could it be that he found the familiarity of Mary's voice relaxing, so natural sounds or gentle music would have worked just as well? We do not know, for this was not a scientific study designed to establish the effects of a therapeutic intervention.

Simulation, distraction or relaxation may all play a part and the question is worth investigating for if we know what helps we will be better placed to avoid the use of sedation when people are resistive or agitated. However, for now it is sufficient to say that simulated presence therapy brought relief to both Peter, a most troubled man, and the nurses who were struggling to meet his needs. Mary was delighted, not only knowing that Peter's violence was now under control but also because it meant he had regained a semblance of dignity. I also think our success motivated her to find out whether her suspicions were justified.

One day Carol was telephoned by one of Peter's cousins. Mary had tracked him down and he had confirmed what she had suspected. Carol was told a story that had not been spoken about for over 60 years. Peter and his cousin had been evacuated together. Two young city boys had found themselves in the countryside living on adjacent farms. Every week they would meet up at the local market and Peter would tell his tales. He would talk about being scolded, shouted at and punished for the smallest of errors or misdemeanours. Sometimes he would talk of beatings. One day he said that they, by which he meant the farmer and his brother, were making him do things he did not want to do. He would say no more because they had told him not to, and for these two insecure and lonely children miles from home you did what grown ups told you, even though what was happening felt very wrong. For nearly a year Peter lived on the farm and we can only imagine what he endured. Whatever that might have been it scarred him for the rest of his life.

Simulated presence therapy was working well. Many of the nurses were talking openly about trying something similar with other residents who were not necessarily aggressive, but who were anxious and unhappy. Could they use cine film or family videos not simply to occupy people but to comfort and help them feel more secure? They saw themselves as both care and therapeutic workers. Carol agreed to look at the care plans to see if simulated presence work might help other residents, but now knowing that he had been abused as a child she wanted to do one more thing for Peter. He was most likely to get worked up when he was being given a strip wash or being undressed. Being seen naked was clearly a trauma he wanted to avoid. Carol reflected on those typical bathing scenes from generations ago and had an idea. She got a sheet, cut a hole for Peter's head, plus two slits at the side to give his arms the freedom to move, and two parallel pairs of diagonal slits at the front and back through which the nurses would be able to wash his body without him having to stand naked in front of them. Wearing the 'modesty sheet' they could also partly dress him then, with his underwear and trousers on, the sheet could be removed with his dignity preserved. This was a final therapeutic touch that showed Peter's arrival in the nursing home was not the failure Mary had spoken of.

Over one third of people with dementia live in care homes not because they have been failed but for the reason that their needs have become so complex and great they require the support only skilled carers can provide at times that for many may be frequent and unpredictable. A caring partner doing the best they can in their own home cannot be expected to do everything that is required as a person's dementia unfolds and it is unreasonable for others to make family carers believe this is how it ought to be. As you might suspect Carol agrees, but importantly so does Mary – and if he could talk to us I have every confidence so would Peter.

&

EIGHTEEN

Not the Nine o'Clock News

"You'll never guess what's going on here?" Mike exclaimed. "I've got a client standing on the toilet and he's trying to climb out of the window. Do you think you could ring back?" And that was how I became involved in the life of Mr and Mrs N.

Mr N's dementia had progressed unremarkably over a number of years. His wife, a bright and energetic woman in her late 70s, had cared for her husband without complaint, until he started to follow her around or, if he failed to see her leave the room, to seek her out. Separation anxiety is one of the most common causes of wandering. Mrs N was a source of reassurance for her husband. Just by being around she provided him with a sense that all was well in a world that was for him becoming ever more mysterious.

"I don't understand why he can't leave me in peace. Following me around all the time, looking for me. It's impossible. I can't even go into the kitchen without him walking behind me. I tell him to sit down and he just stands there. He's had dementia for ages and he never used to be like this. He used to sit in his chair for hour after hour in his own world. I can't believe I used to complain that he didn't do anything. I'd sit in the room with him and nothing. What I would give for some peace now. I don't understand why he's changed. Do you?"

I was taken aback. It appeared that nobody had sat down with Mrs N to explain how her husband's dementia might evolve. Not simply how he would one day be totally dependent on her, but also how he might come to terms with his dementia.

In the beginning of Alzheimer's disease, a problem people have is storing the details of life. It is why during an assessment they are shown pictures to remember or given words to recall. Minutes later they may remember a few, but the rest have been forgotten. Sometimes a person may remember none at all, but they know what they have been asked to do. It is the details that cause the difficulty. In everyday life they would be forgetting what they had intended to do next or where they had put something down, and these could have been the early signs that indicated that something might be wrong.

Eighteen months later they might be given the same assessment tests to do. After being given words or pictures to recall, and being asked about them, the answer is invariably, "What pictures? You didn't show me any pictures." It is now not simply the details of an experience that are not stored, but the entire experience. To that person the event has never happened.

This progression of forgetfulness explained the change

in Mr N's behaviour that his wife was struggling to understand. In the beginning his wife may have said to her husband "I'm just going upstairs to make the bed. I'll be back in a few minutes", and off she would go, leaving Mr N sitting untroubled in the lounge. As the minutes passed, if we were a fly on the wall Mr N might appear to be a touch perplexed. "What did she say she was going to do? Where did she say she was going? When did she say she was coming back?" As he sits in the chair pondering over the details, reassuringly counterbalancing his puzzlement is his ability to recall that his wife said she was doing something nearby and most comforting of all that she said she would return – he simply cannot remember 'the what or the when'. At that moment in through the door walks his wife, and for Mr N all is once again right with the world. For Mrs N she has just spent the last fifteen minutes untroubled, getting on with her jobs.

Eighteen months later, returning to the house, we enter a troubled and darker world. Again Mrs N says "I'm just going upstairs to make the bed. I'll be back in a few minutes" and off she goes. However, as we keep watching Mr N, it starts to feel very different. He no longer comes over as puzzled and pondering. As the seconds pass he appears bewildered and increasingly ill at ease. The woman who he needs to have in sight in order to feel safe has seemingly vanished. His memory has deteriorated. It is no longer the case that he cannot remember the details of what happens: entire experiences are forgotten. Now there had been no reassuring words; the event never happened. There is no recollection of where she might have gone, what she might be doing, how long she has been away and most troubling of all when, or if, she will return. For Mr N his wife is simply absent. Rational thought does not come to his rescue for Mr N's ability to reason, along with many other areas of cognition, is not what it once was.

If we found ourselves in a similar position and a loved one had seemingly disappeared, what would we do? I am in little doubt that we would search for them, and if we did not want to experience abandonment in the first place, follow them wherever they go. And that is exactly what Mr N does – he clings and seeks. He clings to his wife not because he knows that he forgets, for this in itself is no more than a momentary impression. Instead, in his world of grave misgivings, anxious feelings are never far away and the need to feel secure constantly beckons. He follows and searches for his wife not because she is simply a person who is to hand but because emotional memories are not easily erased. Consequently decades of trust, love and affection remain engraved within his brain to ensure that Mr N is, as Oliver Sacks wrote, "moored by her presence, lost without her".

What is a solution for Mr N is suffocating for his wife. She gets no space, no time for herself. She always has to be alert in case he slips outside while trying to find her, and one morning this is what he did. If he had gone upstairs he would have found her, but no, he walked down the hall out through the front-door and down the garden path.

I have been asked many times why in these instances the person does not come to a halt having forgotten why they are on the move. As we know, people with dementia do not only forget what they hear and see, they also forget within minutes, if not seconds, what they are thinking. So would Mr N not forget that he was searching for his wife and simply stop walking?

Well, he most probably does forget his thoughts, but we have to keep in mind what motivated him to search for his wife in the first place - separation anxiety. While the thinking component of anxiety – worry, foreboding, dread – may well fade away, there are also the physiological symptoms to consider – the churning stomach, pounding heart, racing pulse, nausea, trembling and sweaty skin – and these are likely to persist for longer. In fact, the likelihood is that in dementia the physiological signs of anxiety always persist longer than the memory of why the person felt anxious in the first place.

So in the lounge of a care home if one resident hits another, the physiological reaction will last beyond the memory of having being hit. Thus the resident will be sitting there aroused and anxious even though they have no knowledge of why they should feel that way. For Mr N, walking down his garden path, even though he no longer has any recollection of why he is leaving his house he remains anxious and the innate motivation to survive will dominate his actions. If you are moving in one direction with your heart pounding and stomach churning, self-preservation tells you that what has made you feel that way must be behind you, and this ensured that Mr N kept walking down the street around the corner and out of sight even though he had no recall why he was doing so.

Mrs N comes downstairs, the front door is wide open and her heart leaps into her mouth. Is it any wonder she cannot cope and sooner rather than later she finds herself sitting with her family doctor saying: "You've got to help me. I can't go on. I never get a break. If he's not hovering around me, following me wherever I go, he's searching for me. Sometimes I need to go out to the shops or the post office, and I don't always want him with me. I've always got to keep an eye on him. And he can be embarrassing. He calls out, sometimes he goes up to people he doesn't know and twice he has wet himself when we've been out shopping. What am I supposed to do? If I leave him at home he'll be out in the street looking for me and don't tell me to lock him in. There's the fire, the taps, the cooker, the stairs – who knows what he'll get up to?"

The doctor shared her concerns but there were no miracles to offer. She was reluctant to sedate Mr N if for no other reason than she suspected Mrs N would be unable to cope if her husband was to become even more dependent upon her. But she had a suggestion: "Let me have a word with social services, I'm sure they will be able to help." So into the life of Mr and Mrs N came a social worker. He knew what to expect, for the GP's referral described how Mrs N was unable to cope with her husband's wandering.

It was easy to sympathise with Mrs N as she described her worries and the strain she faced day after day. This was the matter to be addressed by the social worker and it was, through Mr N's attendance twice a week at a nearby day centre. On one day Mrs N would have the opportunity to do the jobs she needed to do, and on the other a chance to relax.

This was an understandable, but nevertheless curious

solution. The answer to Mr N's inability to be apart from his wife for seconds was to separate him from her for hours on end and expect him to cope. To appreciate how this proposal was going to have calamitous consequences we have to consider again why Mr N left his chair.

When Mr N had memory for experience, even though he could no longer recall the details of his life, he did not cling to or search for his wife, for his residual ability to remember still allowed him to feel secure in her absence. It was only when he could not even remember the outline of his life that he felt the need to keep his wife in sight – only then was his vulnerability overwhelming. It never was dementia that led him to leave his chair but insecurity; for when he felt secure he stayed where he was and if one day in the future he was able to feel secure once more he would again sit and not trouble his wife. The challenge may be wandering, but the explanation is insecurity; the need to be met is for him to feel secure when his wife is not around. Attendance at a day centre may meet Mrs N's need for rest and respite, but how could it meet Mr N's need for security? This is why he came to be on a toilet seat attempting to climb out of a window.

Mike, the day centre manager, said there was no way that Mr N could continue there. Not because the risks were too great to manage, for that was not Mike's way. It was because it was clear for all to see that Mr N was traumatised by the experience and would continue to be so. However, this would mean the strain of caring being thrown back on to Mrs N with no hope of respite. We all agreed that as Mrs N became more and more exhausted she would not be able to carry on. Within months Mr N

191

would need to be admitted to a care home and it did not take a genius to work out what the consequences of that decision would be for Mr N.

We talked to Mrs N about giving her peace of mind by making her house more secure. We put in a circuit breaker connected to the door bell, which meant that whenever the front door was opened the bell sounded. It was not alarming, but it meant that Mrs N would be alerted to her husband possibly leaving the house and be able to get to the front door before he had got too far, especially as he would be slowed down by the bolt we had fixed to the far side of the gate – a positioning that was unusual, unexpected and which Mr N would be unable to recall.

While these security measures provided some relief it still meant that Mrs N had to be on her guard and her tolerance was now wearing thin. More significantly our intervention did not touch two of Mrs N's other concerns: her wish to go out to the shops sometimes without her husband, and to be free of his suffocating over-powering presence each and every day. To achieve this we would have to address Mr N's need to feel secure and all agreed this was an impossible aspiration.

Mrs N told me that they had been married for 53 years. They had always lived a quiet life. Her husband had worked for the council, "something to do with council tenants and their rents". Like many men of his generation her husband was intelligent but opportunities had not come his way, she said. He had a thirst for knowledge and he used to read voraciously. "Never novels, always heavy books. Biographies, politics, history, that sort of thing."

I also learnt that as a couple they were creatures of habit, especially in their later years. In the evening they would have their evening meal around half past six, make sure the washing up was done and then settle down and watch television. At nine o'clock Mr N would watch the BBC news while Mrs N tidied up the house. Jobs done, she would sit in the kitchen, flick through a magazine and have a bedtime drink, usually a cup of cocoa.

"Why didn't you sit with your husband and watch the news?" I asked.

"He was the intelligent one," she laughed. "When the news was on, well that was it. I think it was like a throwback to the war when everyone used to sit around the radio and listen to the news. All silence and concentration. He wouldn't have been too happy if I'd started to natter. So I'd do a few jobs before going to bed."

"But why stay in the kitchen?"

"Ever since his prostate started to play up he's only had a cup of tea with his evening meal then he wouldn't drink again," she explained. "He didn't want to be up and down all night needing the toilet. I sort of felt guilty drinking in front of him so after I'd tidied up it sort of became a bit of time for me. He'd watch the news and I'd read my magazine. Fifteen minutes at the end of the day to unwind."

Nowadays it was even more important for her to have that time for herself, and she still did, for even though Mr N could remember nothing of what he saw or heard, and probably understood very little, he would still avidly watch the news. He was going through the motions of normality because it was the natural thing to do.

This conversation provided us with the possible key to resolve Mr N's desperate insecurity. Deprived of memory, Mr N was unable to maintain a true sense of security but from what I had found out perhaps it would be possible to create a pseudo-world of normality and peace of mind. In the face of much scepticism - "Not the Nine o'clock News!" – I recorded on a videotape 11 broadcasts of the BBC's nine o' clock news, which as everybody knows starts with a thunderous and instantly recognisable anthem. Eleven half-hour broadcasts back-to-back, with a three minute gap between each. That was it, straightforward, person-centred and easy to implement – but would it work? Despite the incredulity of my colleagues, Mrs N actually thought it might, so the two of us – feeling like furtive conspirators – put it to the test.

I called round at their house one afternoon. Mrs N opened the front door and, as you might expect, at that very moment Mr N appeared in the hall. She had escaped for barely seconds! We went into the lounge and I gave Mrs N the videotape. Nothing was said and we settled down to have a cup of tea together. Mr N sat in an armchair and gazed at me with a pleasant smile on his face. I noticed he had perfect manners and indeed captured in this moment of time you could not imagine the upset he was causing.

Not long after, I excused myself and went into the hall. A couple of minutes later I heard the distinctive anthem of the BBC news and within moments Mrs N and I were sitting at the kitchen table waiting with bated breath. Was Mr N about to join us? For 25 minutes we waited and neither a sight nor sound of her husband was seen or heard. Mrs N went into the lounge and there was her husband intently watching the news. Not only that, he hardly gave her a second glance!

Cautiously confident we embarked on the second stage. What would happen when the news finished? A couple of days later I returned and we ran through it all again, but this time Mrs N did not go to see what her husband was doing. The programme finished and a minute or so later we heard him coming out of the lounge. Where would he head? Upstairs? Toward the front door? Would he appear in the kitchen? We never found out, for within seconds the anthem of the BBC news blared out and he must have walked back into the lounge, for all movement ceased. Mrs N could only contain her joy for minutes before she had to go into the lounge to see what her husband was doing. We went together. I'm not sure he wanted the unrestrained hug. He certainly did not expect it, but Mrs N could not control herself, for there was her husband sitting in the armchair watching the news with the same intent he must have shown during the previous 30 minutes or so.

It is what I had hoped for. With his devastated ability to remember, within minutes of watching the news Mr N could not recall he had done so and hence when he heard the theme music he would head off again to watch it.

Mrs N's life was transformed. She could do housework, work in the garden and have time for herself knowing that whatever time she needed Mr N would be contentedly watching the news. And that is what was equally as important. Mr N's life had also been transformed. He was content. He was enjoying life again. He understood little of what he was watching and remembered nothing but that mattered little. The familiarity of what he was doing meant that once again life felt right. Preoccupied within the ordinariness of his life he was no longer racked with separation anxieties. As a result there was no need for him to follow his wife around, nor was there a need for him to search for her. We had demonstrable evidence of success.

As Mrs N became even more confident that the intervention was working she started to go out knowing that on her return her husband would be sitting in the armchair absorbed in the news. If I recall correctly, the longest she left Mr N – inadvertently I hasten to add – was when she was over the road with a neighbour and two hours passed in a flash. Consumed with guilt she had telephoned me to confess! I reassured her that she had nothing to feel guilty about and by the end of our conversation she had agreed that her actions showed how relaxed she had become. She never was out so long again but that was never to matter. Feeling more in control of her life and that she did now in fact have a life, Mrs N was still caring for her husband 18 months later.

People might say that my work with Mr N was founded on deception, and it was – but what were the alternatives? Sedation? Admission to a care home? To this day I believe that it was not simply a case of Mr N's behaviour being controlled by the BBC's nine o'clock news – rather, his care plan resonated with who Mr N was and as a result gave him hours of satisfaction even if it was a pleasure embedded within his inability to reason and recall.

&

NINETEEN

"How could he do this to me?"

I encountered Roger on four occasions. First, when nobody was sure why his depression would not respond to treatment. Second, when his conduct was not just extreme but on many occasions downright bizarre. Then, years later, when the manager of the care home where he was living said he was going to be given notice to leave if his behaviour did not change; and finally when his distraught wife insisted I see her straight away.

Roger had been a teacher who following early retirement still stayed in touch with the school by organizing and supervising adventure holidays for boys in the sixth form. Swimming, rock climbing, canoeing, trekking, camping, hang gliding – Roger did them all. He loved being outside and despite coming up to 60 he was still thrilled by physical exertion, which was why he was with a group of students climbing in the Pyrenees when he fell and broke both his ankles.

Weeks in plaster did nothing for his mood. Sitting

around the house was never going to suit Roger, and his wife was not unduly surprised as he became more and more irritable. What did surprise her was how his mood failed to lift when the plaster was removed. When the physiotherapist said his ankles had healed well and the orthopaedic surgeon said that aside from the occasional twinge he was as good as new, she thought her husband would soon be back to his previous self – but no.

Roger denied that he was depressed but he clearly was. Maybe the fall had knocked his confidence and made him realise that he could not continue being the same adventurer of old. As he became less and less interested in what was happening around him, his wife told him to go to the GP. He prescribed a course of anti-depressants, and then another, and another until he had to admit that "we need a fresh approach". I was the fresh approach. The GP's letter contained the perceptive comment "there is an oddness about Roger that makes me think there is something sinister unfolding. Do you think it might be dementia? Please could you assess and advise". And so it transpired. Roger was suffering from fronto-temporal dementia.

At our first meeting I was impressed not only by how bland and indifferent he was, but how he was inappropriately over-familiar. He asked me what school I attended, and over and over again, "Do you support Manchester United? I do." The neuropsychological examination revealed marked executive dysfunction (damage to the highest intellectual abilities that enable a person to live an independent and socially appropriate life) and word dysfluency (changes in the speed and ease of producing words) both indicators of fronto-temporal brain damage, while the MRI scan showed marked atrophy more pronounced in the frontal lobes. The timing of the accident had been nothing more than a coincidence.

Months passed and I had had no involvement with Roger until a community psychiatric nurse asked whether I could meet with his wife because she had many questions to ask about her husband's dementia.

Helen was the opposite of Roger. Quiet and unadventurous, she was the perfect foil to his outgoing ways. While he was quenching his thirst for action she was the one who steadied the ship and made sure home life ran smoothly. What she needed to know from me was why Roger was deliberately trying to upset and at times terrorize her. He had thrown her clothes into the garden, threatened her with a hammer and was always argumentative. However, what was upsetting her most of all were the accusations. "He's convinced I'm having affairs, always with men from Blackburn. Not one but loads. He goes on and on about it. How many affairs can a woman have with men from Blackburn, Lancashire?" she said with a wry smile, "And why Blackburn? I've never even been there." I could not answer these questions but I was able to tell Helen how frontal lobe damage is associated with impulsive and disinhibited conduct, poor judgment and impaired reasoning, and perseveration, which meant that Roger could repeat endlessly the same phrase, question or action not because he wanted to but because not all his behaviour was under his control (see also the story of Sylvia in chapter 13).

Helen also talked about how other people often believed what her husband had to say, a state of affairs she found not only annoying, but at times staggering. I suspected we were again talking about men from Blackburn. I explained that I understood how Roger might still be able to create a favourable first impression and hence appear plausible during brief encounters. So far it was only his highest intellectual and language faculties that were damaged, while his essential cognitive and social skills were sufficiently well preserved to enable fleeting contact with friends and neighbours to appear to all intents and purposes normal.

I am not sure whether our meeting helped but it at least prepared Helen for some of what was to unfold in the coming months. She knew it was perseveration when Roger started to say over and over again, "How hard do you want me to hit you?" When he started to only eat raw food but would spend ages dicing fruit and vegetables into tiny morsels, she again knew he was perseverating and held her silence. She was in fact more irritated by having watched him devote what seemed hours of effort to preparing his food he would eat very little and instead would deposit most of it down the toilet. And when she was contacted by the bank manager and insurance broker to be told that her husband had instructed them to remove her name from their bank account and car insurance policy she maintained her composure, explained the nature of his illness and apologised on his behalf.

Close to three years had passed when I was contacted by Helen. Roger had now been living in a specialist residential home for nearly six months and matters had gone from bad to worse. She wondered whether I could speak to the home manager, who was at her wits' end.

The manager said she did not want to give Roger notice to leave, because she knew it had happened once before, but his behaviour was intolerable and she had to think of the other residents. From the moment he had arrived he rarely sat for long but would spend his day earnestly pacing the building. He had a set route that took him from one door to another, and having pulled at the 'baffled' door handles he would walk on to the next. Roger no longer spoke but if you attempted to speak to him he would simply stare at you. It was a look that conveyed his impatience, for all he wished you to do was to step aside so he could carry on with his travels. Additional healthcare monies had been allocated that allowed a carer to accompany him to the local garden centre and to visit the local park, but this did not diminish his need to walk.

With the home's large communal spaces and curved corridors that unfolded before you, Roger's walking was not a problem. Unfortunately when he began to walk into other residents' bedrooms and remove their possessions it was no longer seen as such – their belongings were destined to end up in whichever toilet he came across first. This was the behaviour that had placed Roger beyond the pale. Immune to reasoning, dismissive of stern words, Roger could not be stopped. Unsurprisingly there were struggles and arguments with relatives. Day after day possessions, toilet rolls, towels, books and magazines were not so much disappearing down the toilet as blocking it, causing overflows, slippery floors and unsavoury aromas to plague the home. It was not only the residents' families who were up in arms; the maintenance man said if something was not done he would have no time to do anything other than carry out running repairs to the toilets.

Helen told me that after our last meeting, Roger had quietened down until out of the blue he became fascinated by junk mail. Over the months that followed, piles of brochures and leaflets appeared around the house. When out he would accept each and every offer of a free newspaper and in the supermarket he would pick up all sorts of promotional material, all to be carefully stacked up in neat piles. As Helen began to find the piles and piles of papers increasingly oppressive, Roger turned full circle and over a period of no more than a few days he threw all the papers out. When the wastepaper basket in the lounge and the pedal bin in the kitchen were full to overflowing, he threw the papers out of the window into the front garden. From then on Roger could not tolerate clutter. It was as if he could not bear anything disturbing the good order tidiness represented. If Helen did not get to the post first, into a bin it would go. Roger's idea of helping to put the shopping away was to throw it out. It got so intrusive that if Helen made herself a cup of tea and happened to place it beside her, if Roger spotted it he would clear it away even before she had taken a mouthful.

It started to dawn on her that magazines were missing as well as the cookery book she had left in the kitchen and the novel she had left on the bedside table. When she next put the rubbish out there they were, nestling in the wheelie bin. It occurred to her that Roger had not been filling the bins indoors as he had once done. That was because he was now attracted to the wheelie bin, perhaps because the clutter was out of sight and importantly out of mind, and this brought him the relief he craved. One day Helen counted the number of times Roger brought the wheelie bin to the back door: 29. Once it was to drop in a cotton wool bud he had discovered in the bathroom.

In the care home Roger was again motivated by the need to be free of chaos. As the complaints intensified the manager resisted demands from some families to lock the bedroom doors. You can understand why they were asking for this because what was to Roger nothing other than clutter was a treasured belonging to them and their parent or partner. However, the manager rightly informed them that some residents liked to spend time in their rooms, while others simply wished to visit them during the day and people could neither be locked in or out of their rooms. She explained that it was not as if any of the residents had the capacity to take responsibility for securing and unlocking their doors whenever they wished to do so.

But what was to be done? If Roger could not be stopped from taking people's possessions, toilet rolls and all the rest, could he at least be prevented from putting them down the toilet? The staff placed wastepaper baskets all around the home. Roger studiously ignored them and continued to stuff everything and anything down the toilets. Placing 'rubbish' in the baskets was not sufficient as it remained in sight so it continued to torment him.

Without knowing it, the staff had attempted to use 'functional displacement' to resolve Roger's challenging behaviour, but had unwittingly found how difficult it is. As was said in chapter 10 (the story of Mr D), for it to work the new activity must not require more effort, it needs to be readily available and crucially it must have the same meaning to the person. Using wastepaper baskets did not have functional equivalence because Roger could still see the clutter.

Taking this on board you could see why Roger chose to use the toilets to dispose of his clutter. There were many available, all close at hand and both in function and design they shared much with a wheelie-bin. Not only was each toilet a vessel, even if he could not flush away the items by closing the lid the untidiness was out of sight. If Roger was going to persist in his efforts to tidy the home, and for the foreseeable future this was inevitable, there was clearly only one option. We had to introduce a therapeutic wheelie-bin.

The maintenance man was a marvel. He attached a large kitchen pedal bin to a two-wheel trolley that he used to take boxes and crates to the storeroom. He even sprayed the bin grey and painted an insignia in gold on the lid so it looked like a council crest. One morning it was placed in the corridor outside Roger's bedroom door. Initially he ignored it but over the next few days he was seen placing a few items in the bin. In time, as we had hoped, he would use nothing else. We had achieved functional equivalence. He was still as determined to remove all and sundry but we had provided Roger with a more acceptable way of meeting his need.

In the beginning he would walk back and forward to the bin, and then he started to wheel it around with him. Curiously, at the end of the day or at the end of a busy session collecting and disposing, he never left the wheelie-bin outside his bedroom door. Instead he would park it next to the fire exit at the end of his bedroom corridor, as if he had left it by the back door at home. Of course, the responsibility of the staff was at every opportunity to discreetly take everything Roger had gathered out of the bin and return it all to its rightful place. Combined with sensible procedures such as closing doors where appropriate, putting valuables away in drawers and placing items out of reach on shelves, to the delight of Helen and the home manager the crisis passed.

In contrast to his recent past, Roger continued to live out his days in the home uneventfully and as expected became increasingly frail and passive. For me my involvement was over and so it was a surprise when out of the blue Helen telephoned desperately asking for an appointment. She could not wait a couple of weeks; she needed to see me now. I could not imagine that Roger was in any physical condition to be provoking anyone, but why else would Helen need to see me so urgently?

Helen was crestfallen. As she walked into my office she had no time for social niceties. "Something awful's happened. Roger's left everything, the house, his savings to an animal sanctuary." Roger had died at the weekend and only now had Helen found out that he had changed his will, and she was no longer his beneficiary. All that was his he had left to an animal charity. Aside from having had a couple of cats during their marriage, he had never shown any interest in pets or animals. "It's almost impossible to imagine what he's done. Why would he do this?"

"I am as bewildered as you," I responded, "but maybe in those early days he needed you so much he was scared of losing you. I can't be sure, but possibly his dementia meant that what he feared most became the reality he dreaded and you got the full force of his anger and recriminations. Remember the accusations and the threats?" Of course she did and deep down she knew what Roger had done was the result of his illness, but in truth this was not the question she needed to have answered. The reason why she was beside herself with worry was that Roger had changed his will the month before I first met him. We all knew what happened in the years that followed but he had visited the solicitor before he was diagnosed. Would that not mean that the revised will would be seen as a valid document and she would lose everything? This is why she was so desperate.

Helen left my office in a much better frame of mind. I had assured her that even though I had not known Roger at the time, the results of the examination had shown sufficient impairment of reasoning and judgement, as well as poor impulse control, that there would be no difficulty arguing that these failings would have been similarly extant during the weeks before. Roger's change of heart would be seen for what it was, another early sign of his illness and the will would be declared null and void; and that is how it turned out.

There was much that was tragic during Roger's life with dementia and it may only have been one aspect of his story but it was gratifying to know that for a period of time people had felt able to let him be. Empathy and ingenuity allowed him to pursue his need to live a life free of clutter. Being allowed to walk and 'do' with no demands, interference or enquiry meant that for a time he was able to find a wordless quiet within which to be himself.

TWENTY

It's why he became a teacher

In the space of a few weeks, years of principled intentions, earnest proposals and at long last actual change were placed in jeopardy by the actions of two men, both of whom knew nothing of the parts they were playing.

A dynamic and far-sighted director of social services had proposed the opening of four specialist residential dementia care units that would allow the hospital to close some of its long-stay beds. In turn the hospital trust was to provide two multi-professional community mental health teams to lead the modernisation of services for older people and to buttress a team of dedicated homecare workers who would support people with dementia in their own homes. There was the expected outcry from some GPs who did not want the added responsibility of caring for people with dementia in the community, from certain psychiatrists and nurses who did not wish to see the loss of hospital wards, and even from local carers' groups who feared the loss of in-patient beds. Even within social services there were those who felt that hospitals were the best place to care for people with serious dementia, especially those who were challenging.

The first unit, attached to a block of sheltered flats, opened with 12 residents admitted from the nearby hospital. In the first week disaster struck. Mr A, a man with dementia, slipped off the unit and made his way along the link corridor to a ground-floor lounge where he was promptly chased out by an elderly tenant gesticulating with his walking stick. Nobody saw what happened next, but the elderly tenant was discovered lying on the floor in the corridor with Mr A standing close by holding the walking stick. The tenant was admitted to hospital and died two days later. The worst fears of many people were confirmed, in particular those closest to the incident, the tenants. We had spent weeks reassuring and pacifying them, saying their lives would not be affected and then this had happened. Mr A was returned to hospital, and Mr G arrived in his place. He was admitted from home where he had lived with his wife. He had no history of troublesome behaviour, yet as soon as he arrived he started to act out.

It was said that he was unpredictably violent. I was told he would sit in the lounge disoriented, uncommunicative and at times intimidating simply by the way he looked at you. Worst of all he would assault carers for no reason. In less than a month three members of staff were off sick, one with a fractured cheek bone, all after having been attacked by Mr G. There was no one on the staff team who was not wary of him, and a few were so fearful they wanted nothing to do with him.

Given the significance of his behaviour, the implications of which extended far beyond the trials of the care assistants working on the unit, I was asked whether there was anything that could be done to prevent an admission to hospital for this would constitute a death knell for the project.

We embarked upon a two-week behavioural analysis of Mr G's behaviour. I wanted to see how frequently Mr G was violent and importantly whether his violence really was unpredictable. After nine days the team leader asked whether they could stop recording: "Take it from me, he's violent. We're being battered black and blue." In those nine days Mr G had been violent 47 times.

There was no doubt Mr G was unacceptably violent but the behavioural analysis had revealed that his violence was not unpredictable. On 96 per cent of occasions Mr G was violent while he was receiving intimate personal care. It was nearly always if those actions were to do with his toileting, for example prompting him to use the toilet, checking to see if he had wet himself or trying to change him because he had. He rarely assaulted other residents, visitors or staff aside from when intimate care was involved.

It was equally clear that the actions of the staff were not maintaining his violence for their responses were varied and unpredictable. Sometimes they persisted in their actions to care for him, at other times they would walk away, recoil or scold him. On the odd occasion they would attempt to restrain him. The absence of consistent consequences showed that he was not acting out in order to gain a desired reaction. However, even if the care assistants' actions had been consistent, these could not have motivated his violence for in common with all people with severe dementia Mr G could hardly retain information for more than moments and hence he could never have any recollection of people's responses to his behaviour.

The results of the behavioural analysis provided us with two questions to address. First, why did Mr G show no interest in using the toilet? If we were able to answer this and do something about it we would in one fell swoop dramatically reduce the likelihood of violence. Unfortunately the layout of the unit left much to be desired. The two communal toilets were away from the main living area, tucked down a corridor and obscured by ubiquitous magnolia paint. With such poor visual access, wherever Mr G sat in the lounge it would not be possible for him to see a toilet. But why had he never made any effort to find a toilet? To answer this we had to discover Mr G, and as we did the pieces of his story fell into place.

Mr G had been a teacher, ending his career as deputy headmaster at the school where he had worked for 27 years. Describing her husband, his wife was not especially flattering. He was reserved and conservative, stubborn and taciturn. "You would never say he was fun to be with. He really didn't have a sense of humour." Sombre and serious would sum him up. While he was in his element addressing a school assembly or overseeing a parents-teachers evening, he was ill at ease in company for small talk was not for him. He was not a 'people person' and unfortunately he made matters worse for himself by not only being aloof but also coming over as somewhat pompous. Keeping up appearances was also all-important to him. He would often say "if a job's worth doing it's worth doing well". Life as Mrs G had not been easy.

Unsurprisingly for such an introverted and private man, his passion was a solitary pursuit. Away from work he would spend summer evenings, holidays, and even crisp winter days contentedly busying himself in his garden for hours on end. "Our garden was beautiful. It was where he was happiest."

At school he did not cope well with setbacks, often losing perspective and consequently work often caused him to have periods of morose disenchantment, during which he was even more likely to be disillusioned with people. As we conjured up a picture of a not especially pleasing personality his wife introduced a sense of balance by posing a pertinent rhetorical question. "You have to ask yourselves, why do you think he wanted to be a teacher?" To control and dominate, to shelter behind rules and defined boundaries or to help others learn and develop? She assured us it was the latter. "He always enjoyed studying, and if he saw students listening and learning and then wanting to know more it brought him a lot of pleasure. You see he nearly always had good intentions but he didn't do himself any favours." Unfortunately, while he did not wish to cause offence and invariably he wanted to help, his manner was frequently misunderstood, and as a result people rarely warmed to him.

Mr G was clearly not a man who was going to prosper in residential care. A proud and insular man, he was never going to be comfortable receiving intimate care that he would experience as an inexplicable invasion of his privacy. As a man accustomed to being in authority, when he said 'no' he really meant it, and if staff persisted in helping him you could see how his anger might spill over into 'out-of-character' but explicable rage. But why was he wetting himself in the first place?

He drew no attention to the fact that he might need the toilet. He would simply remain in his chair, wet himself and then be discovered soiled. However, incontinence was unlikely, for his wife said he was using the toilet at home right up until the day he came to live on the unit. It was his wife's poor health that had led to his admission rather than any dramatic deterioration in her husband's behaviour. I suspected it was again to do with his personality.

Mr G possessed a conservative outlook which I imagine meant he never relished taking risks or making mistakes. Such an introverted man would always have felt awkward asking "where's the toilet?". With no knowledge of where the toilets were, these elements of Mr G's personality conspired against him and he sat motionless in his chair destined to degrade himself. When discovered, or if a member of staff enquired whether he needed the toilet, it constituted an affront to his dignity and a confrontation would ensue.

What were the care assistants to do? The challenge was that Mr G was presenting staff with two sets of needs that were mutually exclusive – whichever way they turned, Mr G was going to suffer. His need for hygiene could only be met with assistance, such as accompanying him to the toilet. This would, however, violate his need for privacy and self-respect and result in a violent reaction. However, if they addressed his need to be left alone they would fail to meet his need for hygiene and Mr G would soil himself. The tragedy for Mr G was that his dementia did not allow him to see the inevitable degrading consequences of his own efforts to preserve his dignity.

There was no way that Mr G's physical care could be neglected so a care plan was required that would permit staff to reconcile Mr G's need to be assisted to the toilet with his need to be free of unwelcome attention. 'Impossible' was the general opinion. Some were already talking about using incontinence pads, but this would be condemning Mr G to never ending indignity, while doing little to resolve the risk that staff would continue to be assaulted.

The environment was not about to become more legible, so was it possible to draw on what we knew about Mr G to fashion a care plan that he might accept? After many hours I proposed a plan which in its simplicity belied the amount of time it took to devise. Two days later the new care plan commenced and in the two weeks that followed Mr G was violent on just six occasions. The relief was palpable and the sense of achievement immense. We had shown that you could work therapeutically with people whose behaviour was challenging, so what had been done?

The sensory garden provided me with the hope of achieving change. Gardening had been Mr G's passion, an interest that had fulfilled him for hours on end. Why should it be different now? If Mr G's enthusiasm for gardening remained undimmed within the recesses of his mind, could we use this as a way of getting him to the toilet? If we could, his dressing skills would permit him to be left alone to use the toilet discreetly.

As it was not possible to establish a pattern to the incidents of wetting I suggested a rigid toileting programme be introduced. Every two hours Mr G was to be approached but with no initial mention of the word 'toilet'. This was a relief to many of the carers, who were so intimidated by Mr G they did not want to mention it in his presence. Instead, the topic to be talked about was the garden. I heeded the words of his wife and suggested we added something to the approach. Why had Mr G been attracted to teaching? It was because he wanted to help people learn, that is what gave him the greatest pleasure. This is why he became a teacher and this is what the care plan embraced. In the process we reversed the disempowerment so commonly observed in the care of people with dementia wherein too many are told what to do, when to do it and with whom they are going to do it.

Mr G was to be placed in a position of authority and his advice sought – do the roses need pruning, were they weeds or flowers, does the lawn need mowing or the bugs exterminating? We had blended his status with his joy of gardening.

Mr G understood a fair amount, even though he said little, and much of what he had to say would quickly tail off into incomprehensible utterances. He responded beyond all our expectations. Without saying a word he would rise from his chair and readily accept the arm that was offered more out of courtesy than necessity. He was assisted along the corridor toward the garden, all the time being reminded where they were heading. The route ensured he would walk past the two communal toilets. On reaching the first, if he was accompanied by a male carer, the latter would say, "I'm nipping in to the toilet before we go into the garden, are you coming in?" For an enthusiastic gardener of his generation this would be customary practice. He could be outside for hours and would not want to be caught short and have to walk back through his house wearing muddy boots because he desperately needed the toilet. He would have gone to the toilet first.

If he was being accompanied to the toilet by a female carer, she would say, "I've just been to the toilet. Do you need the toilet before we go into the garden? We could be outside for sometime." On nearly all occasions, regardless who was accompanying him, Mr G would use the toilet and as we anticipated without needing any assistance.

After using the toilet he was reminded that they were heading off to the garden and how grateful they were for his help. On the first occasion, several of us could not help but look out from the lounge window as Mr G gazed at the flowers and foliage with obvious delight. Composed and slightly smiling, his manner was 'alive', and a gentler, more peaceful air surrounded him. He was always to relish the experience. After a few minutes if Mr G showed no interest in returning indoors he could be left outside in the knowledge that the perimeter was secure and a watchful eye could be kept on him.

Two hours later he was approached again and a fresh episode would unfold. Some of the care assistants were unconvinced. "It might work once or twice but he'll soon see through what we are doing," was a common refrain. However, this was never going to happen for so severe was his dementia Mr G could remember nothing for more than a few seconds, let alone what had occurred two hours earlier. Other staff were convinced that he would flare up as soon as it was suggested he use the toilet, while some could not see why he would agree to go into the toilet simply because he was heading into the garden. Eventually they appreciated we had tapped into the well of who Mr G had not only been but who he remained, and as a result what was being asked of him was not incongruent or superficial but reflected his innermost self.

For 19 months the care plan met Mr G's needs. In the winter the small greenhouse was the salvation – not for Mr G who was perfectly happy to venture outside in any weather, but for the staff who did not share his disregard for inclement weather. However, the inevitable happened and Mr G succumbed to frailty. No longer able to walk far, the journey to the garden became too arduous, but in his weakened state he was no longer resistive and instead accepted the care he needed. He never became the most popular resident on the unit, but he had gained the respect of staff who had seen another side of him, a side that warranted respect. The care team had learnt there was more to dementia care than most had thought and as a result they were now more likely to listen to residents and regard each of them as people with their own individual personalities and life histories, yet at face value all we had done was to implement a rigid toileting programme.

There is a postscript to Mr G's story. On the fourth day following the start of the programme I was in the lounge talking to the team leader and I saw a care assistant talking to Mr G and then accompanying him out of the room.

Just minutes later the care assistant returned with Mr G. "Didn't he want to go?" the team leader asked.

"No, he's been." Believing she had not made herself clear she added, "I mean he's been to the toilet." "But what about the garden?" the team leader enquired, fixing the care assistant with a quizzical stare. She acknowledged they had not been to the garden.

"But that's the care plan, toilet then into the garden."

Not on this occasion. There were lots of things she had to do and so there was no time. The care assistant reiterated that she had taken Mr G to the toilet and importantly he had used it. For her it was transparently clear that this was the be all and end all.

Astutely the team leader said , "Look at Mr G now and ask yourself: over the next few minutes do you think he will enjoy himself as much sitting in that chair as he would be doing if you'd taken him into the garden?" As she spoke you could see the penny dropping. The care assistant was appreciating what she had done. She had betrayed Mr G by taking advantage of his inability to remember. She had not been abusive or cruel, but had shown herself to be insensitive with little regard for what the care plan truly meant. She saw the trip to the garden simply as a reward for having used the toilet, a reward she could withhold if time did not allow because she knew he would be unable to recollect what had been said. But it was not and never had been intended to be a reward for compliance, for how could Mr G be rewarded for what he could not remember doing?

All people need to have a reason to get up in the morning and while his dementia would always mean that he never knew life was now more pleasurable we had designed a care plan that meant something to Mr G. Each day he had the opportunity to be in the garden for maybe an hour. He could never look forward with anticipation, never reflect on what he had enjoyed, but there was now reason to be alive. Each time he entered the garden he encountered a vista he had never seen before but this in no way took away the sheer joy of being where he belonged. The care assistant never had too little time again.

&

TWENTY ONE

Angela's nose

Imagine a care home that runs like clockwork. Regimented to the point where the distinctive ways of each and every resident are squeezed out of existence. One where the inflexible routines and care practices benefit the smooth running of the home rather than the needs of anybody who lives there – aside that is from their personal care needs, for there is no privation of care where physical interventions are concerned. In this home there is a preoccupation with cleanliness, appearance and safety. As a result the freedom of residents is limited and the time of care assistants is taken up with a never ending cycle of basic bodily care and domestic tasks. With little spare time, contact between carers and residents is always functional and perfunctory. Residents do not experience life, for in no meaningful sense of the word is there any. Instead residents endure a futile and loveless existence. This is where Jack lives and where Angela works.

Angela's nose has been broken. Not in a fall, or by

walking inadvertently into a door, but by Jack, who for no reason punched her as she was trying to help him. "I did nothing wrong." He had wet himself. She had gone over to change him and as she said "let's get you out of those clothes", he lashed out, punching her in the face, breaking her nose.

Forty residents live in the home and every day is the same. First thing in the morning the task is to get everybody out of bed and into the dining room ready for breakfast. There are four corridors, each with ten bedrooms, and with the exception of the home manager who usually finds herself in the office and one carer who is based in the dining room, all the care assistants would be in one corridor getting everybody out of bed. That is the routine: work one corridor at a time. The corridor where Jack sleeps is very busy. There are staff in residents' rooms getting people out of bed, sometimes working in pairs helping residents out of their clothes, into the toilet, washing and then dressing them for the day ahead. There are carers walking up and down, some taking residents to the dining room, others returning to get more ready for the day. The 'hustle and bustle' disturbs some residents who come out of their rooms in their night clothes, one of whom is Jack. A few residents appear from other parts of the building, drawn to the corridor by all the noise that is inevitable when there is such feverish activity. There is only so much time allocated to each corridor, for breakfast has to be served at 8.30 a.m. when all 40 residents have to be in the dining room.

Angela was getting someone ready for the day and she could hear Jack shouting in the corridor. The care team considered Jack to be a nuisance: "He's always calling out. Shouting the same thing over and over again. It's always the same – 'I'm fed up with this place. This isn't my home and I don't want to be here anymore.' It's like a mantra reverberating around the home." This morning was no different. He had been shouting for ages and Angela admitted "he was trying my patience". She later described Jack as being "noisy, confused, incontinent and violent" that morning.

Having got her resident ready for the day, Angela walked her along the corridor where Jack was still standing. As she passed by he gestured toward her and again started to call out "I'm fed up with this place. I don't..." and Angela did as everybody else had done: she ignored him. It was as if Jack did not exist.

Angela returned to get somebody else out of bed, and there was Jack standing motionless, head bowed, saying nothing. As she was about to walk past, Angela noticed he had wet himself. "I couldn't leave him like that so I decided to get him ready next. I stopped and I think I was about to get hold of his arm but I got no chance. I said something like, 'come on let's get you out of those clothes' and he hit me. For no reason, he just hit out and punched me. You can tell me I did something wrong, but I can't see it."

If not wrong, her actions were to be revealed as unthinking and insensitive. However, what I call care malignancies can be embedded so deep within the cultural normality of dementia care they pass unseen.

Angela said that Jack was noisy and that was not in question. He had been calling out for ages. She also said he was confused because he was shouting this was not his home when he had no other home. He had been living in the care home for nearly a year, having struggled to fend for himself as his dementia progressively worsened. However, while Jack's words were in accord with my definition of confusion – "the reporting of information or living an experience that represents a reality different to our own", such as asking to go home when already at home – if there was ever a group of people who say what they do not mean and mean what they do not say it is those with dementia.

I do not believe Jack was confused, because of what happened next. What can appear to be confusion can actually be an attempt to communicate an unmet need. A person may, for example, be demanding to go to work not because that is where they know they must be but because they are bored, or they may ask for their mother not because they know her to be alive but because they are frightened and need to be comforted. Jack was shouting out that he was fed up; this was not his home and he did not want to be there anymore not because he knew he lived somewhere else but because he wanted the toilet. "I am fed up with this place, this isn't my home. The toilet should be there and it's not. *I need the toilet!*"

The speech used by people with dementia can contain hidden messages; sometimes, as John Killick has observed, "the language used... is a metaphorical one". We have to ask ourselves what a person's words might mean. It may not just be the words that are spoken which are important, the number of times they are said may also be significant for repetition of particular words or phrases may reflect a key theme to be picked up. Tone of voice, intonation, facial expression and body posture can all help as well to aid our understanding. Unfortunately Jack was shouting into an unsympathetic and unhearing void. Negative attitudes held sway.

It logically followed that if Jack was calling out for the toilet he could not have been incontinent. Two of the labels Angela used were erroneous – but what about Jack's violence? That was undeniable. She had been attacked – but was it without reason?

Many incidents of violence, abuse and resistance result in a carer or nurse saying "What did I do to deserve this?". However, if you map many of these incidents, a malign sequence of events, an unseen pathway, unfolds and with Angela it was no different. An act of care typically takes only a few seconds. This is insufficient time for a carer to monitor their thoughts and actions. Following an assault there is nothing to reflect upon other than the original good intention. That's why, as with Angela, the inevitable conclusion is "I did nothing wrong"; the attack was unwarranted; it must be because he has dementia.

Angela had shown no empathy for what Jack had experienced and how he was feeling. When he was calling out she had ignored him. She paid no heed to his frustration and anger. She was only prepared to give him time when he presented her with a physical care task to be done. While Angela had no wish to leave him in a sorry state I think that was more to do with him being clean rather than feeling his humiliation.

Angela had clearly assumed that Jack knew who she was and hence would readily accept all she was about to do, when the reality for Jack was that he knew nothing of the sort. This is confirmed by the fact that she did not introduce herself in any way, but proceeded straight to the task at hand. In his state of 'not knowing' every step toward him would have been inexplicable. He would have been unable to fathom why Angela was approaching, and mysterious intent can easily spill over into possible threat. The risk of violence was growing unseen.

Angela did not have the luxury of time for there was too much to do. She was in a hurry and it did not occur to her that it would be best to pause and slowly approach the now demoralised Jack. Coming ever closer within the fleetest of moments Angela was on the cusp of entering Jack's personal space, that invisible ring of security we craft around ourselves and then do our utmost to preserve as ours and ours alone. Unless an invitation is offered, to have that space violated feels uncomfortable, can be threatening and may even be resisted. Jack had offered no invitation, for why would he? To him Angela was a stranger whose intentions were unfolding mysteriously and rapidly before him. Wary and suspicious, he would neither have understood nor wished to see Angela's hands reaching out to him. Then she spoke, "Let's get you out of those clothes."

An early sign of Alzheimer's disease is literal, concrete thinking. It is why a clock drawing test is used as a screening tool for dementia. In early dementia, when asked to set the time to '10 past 11' you observe hesitancy and maybe error. To place the hand on the number '2' feels wrong because there before them on the clock face is '10' and the instruction is to set the hands to '10 past'.

The 'dementia pull' attracts the person to the '10' but this also feels wrong for there is something about '10 past' that suggests the hand should go elsewhere. Hesitancy ensues, and as dementia becomes more severe it is more likely the error will be made and the time will be wrongly set to '10 to 11'. Similarly people with dementia also struggle with a similarities test. For example, when asked in what way an apple and banana are alike many say they are not. "One's round, the other is curved." As soon as the apple and banana are placed in their mind's eye, in the absence of a capacity to think in the abstract the concrete differences are clear to see and any similarity ("they are both fruit") is not.

When Jack heard Angela say, "Let's get you out of those clothes," that is exactly what he expected to happen. In a corridor alive with people and activity this woman was going to remove his clothes because that is what she had just said. Is it any wonder that Jack, perplexed and bemused, now hearing that his clothes were about to come off, lashed out to protect himself and unfortunately connected with Angela's nose? He had not meant to, but neither had Angela intended to convey the impression that she was about to disrobe Jack in public – for it was not only Jack who had said what he did not mean.

What Angela had meant to say was, "Let's get you out of those clothes after I have accompanied you to the privacy of your bedroom where I'll be able to give you a helping hand." Who speaks like that? However in dementia care we need to be mindful that all around is puzzling, baffling and bewildering to those who are being cared for and we must do our best not to add to the mystery by communicating in ways that are ambiguous and misleading.

Angela listened to my analysis and her defences soon came down. She appreciated what she had done. She had regarded Jack more as an object rather than a person. "I've never even thought of seeing what goes on here through their eyes." She told me that Jack often soiled himself and she regretted ignoring his calls, dismissing them as confused irrelevancies. The cursory way she related to Jack also hit home. There was never any time for the residents. If life was going to be different for Jack and the other residents the home could no longer be run on rigid institutional lines.

What significantly contributed to the poor life quality endured by every resident day after day was a focus on when people ate, where they ate and what they wore at mealtimes. A desire to promote resident welfare was in reality serving to achieve the opposite: did it really matter whether people were still in their night clothes when they had breakfast? Why did people have to eat in the dining room, why not in their own rooms? Could there not be a 24-hour menu of snacks and 'light bites' allowing people to live more varied lives? If these changes happened there would be so much less pressure on staff they would discover more time to be with residents rather than always having to do something to or for them.

And so it turned out. After years of stultifying routine, radical change happened. As months passed you could see that the residents, who were now seen as people with disparate needs and feelings mattered more, while routines counted for less, and all because of Angela's broken nose. Yet why was Angela's injury a catalyst for such transformation?

Every day without fail the manager was to be found in the office working through emails, policies and paperwork but on the morning of the assault three care assistants had phoned in sick and she had no option but to get out there and work alongside her hard pressed care assistants. Something she had not done in years. That is why Angela – the person responsible for the task-centred, time-determined culture of care which was draining the life out of the very people to whom she thought she was showing compassion and concern – found herself walking towards Jack, unaware that she was soon to reap a harsh consequence of what she had sown. As for Jack, he was never left to cry out unheard again.

&

TWENTY TWO

A room of one's own

Penny K hated being in the lounge. Confined to her chair, she showed by every aspect of her behaviour that it was so. Severely disabled by vascular dementia, she would call out unintelligibly, curse the person sitting next to her and glare at those who passed too close. In the four months Penny had lived in the care home she had never been violent, but there was always an undercurrent of anger that made you think that one day if she was pushed too far she might lash out.

But what would being pushed too far mean? The people against whom she vented her anger did not deserve to be intimidated by Penny. They were doing no more than be in her presence. Nonetheless, that was enough for Penny. Mealtimes were a nightmare for everybody. She was too distracted by the other residents sitting at the table to concentrate on eating. As you might expect she shouted and cursed, but being in such close proximity to others she took every opportunity to upset and agitate those who were an anathema to her. She would push their plates off the table and knock their drinks over. Recriminations and bedlam would ensue. To the disquiet of her family, staff insisted she stay in the lounge and have her meals alone. While Penny did not seem to mind having her meal served on a tray her family certainly did. Her children in particular saw it as evidence that their mother was being ostracized and complained bitterly. As a result Penny returned to the dining area and the turmoil continued.

Penny was repelled by the characteristics of the people she lived alongside. Without self-awareness, she saw them as distasteful, repugnant and most of all alien. I was confident this was so, because Penny was only offensive in their company. When alone, with her family, with carers and significantly, even with people she had never seen before – and it did not matter whether they be social workers, doctors or relatives of other residents – she was placid, unobjectionable and well-mannered.

It was crystal clear to everybody who worked in the home that Penny was offended by the other residents, so why was it that everyday she found herself in the lounge? Well, that is what staff ensure happens every day in countless care homes across the country. At the beginning of the day residents are helped out of bed, washed, dressed, accompanied to the dining room for breakfast and then on to the lounge where they will spend their days in the company of people who they will often perceive as individuals with whom they have nothing in common. Yet by doing this staff are denying residents what we all treasure – a place of our own. Ever since childhood we have valued knowing such a place exists. Somewhere we can go to be alone, to lose ourselves in dreams, even somewhere to escape to. These feelings are not surrendered as we age. In a care home even more significantly a resident's room is the bridge between what was and what is now.

On numerous occasions I have asked carers and nurses: if you lived in a care home where would you like to spend your days? In your room among what is yours – possessions that resonate with memories, photographs that tap into a well of emotion, your music gently playing in the background – or in the unfamiliarity of a lounge in the midst of strangers who act in ways you rarely if ever comprehend? I have never heard anyone say, "Sit me in the lounge. Next to that woman who wets herself, opposite that man who keeps removing his clothes." So why do those same staff persist in taking residents to communal lounges seemingly in the belief that is where they wish to be? I believe the answers are grounded in the traditions of institutional care.

Until a decade or so ago people with dementia spent their final months, if not years, in psychiatric asylums living on open-plan hospital wards where all that was theirs was the bed, the locker and the cubicle curtain. Every moment, awake or asleep, they were on social display, denied a change of scene and comfort. Eventually this was deemed unacceptable and lounges, often equally as austere as the ward they were joined to, were introduced and accordingly this is where everybody was accompanied, encouraged or taken to: into the 'day room' to spend their time sitting in armchairs exposed to little else other than the background drone of the television that was on from morning until night.

When the National Health Service abandoned all responsibility for providing people with living space, the asylums and geriatric hospitals were demolished and the permanent care of people with dementia was displaced to a rapidly expanding care home sector. In the beginning nursing homes were built and then residential care homes. For both the template was the residential home that had been historically provided by local authorities and voluntary groups, and that had a residents' lounge. But times change.

The photographs from Peter Townsend's study of care homes in the late 1950s show you had to be able to walk and be all but independent to enter a residential care home. If you were not, you would be admitted into hospital care. This meant to be in a lounge was to be in the company of people, more than likely from your neighbourhood with whom you could chat, reminisce and gain a sense of belonging. To be there would have been companionable and importantly everyone was able to choose when they entered and left the lounge for a stroll or to go to their room. This is not what is seen in care homes today where the level of dependency and complex needs approximate to what was once observed on hospital wards. However, it was never the severity of dementia that meant people had to come together in a lounge to be cared for. It was to offer an alternative to the dispiriting and grim ward where they would otherwise have spent their days.

In contemporary care, people with severe dementia no longer live in dormitories but have the comfort and privacy of their own rooms to enjoy. On their arrival in a care home, people and their families are encouraged to personalize the room with possessions. They are asked to bring in pictures, photographs, mementos, ornaments, a bedspread, a television, even small items of furniture. These familiar things not only provide pleasure, but also give rise to a sense of security that comes from feeling this is where you belong. Nowadays it is this which people are being separated from when they are put in the lounge.

The conclusion to be drawn is inescapable. If a person wants to stay in their room it should not automatically be seen as an unhealthy desire indicative of isolation, withdrawal and depression – instead it can be an understandable and appropriate wish for familiarity, continuity and privacy. We are not talking about bare bedrooms but rooms enriched with entertainment and the nostalgic trivia of people's lives.

I explained this all to Penny's family and suggested that maybe she would be better off if she whiled away her days in her room. Their response was not to like my suggestion one little bit.

"This is all spin," her daughter said, "We all know the problems mum causes in the lounge. But it's not her fault. She gets all worked up and she can't help herself. All you want to do is to keep her out of the way. You want to isolate her down a corridor so nobody can see her. It's nothing to do with giving her a better quality of life."

This was understandable, for the earlier decision to give Penny her meals in the lounge had smacked of a punishment. I again made it clear that some people were troubled, sometimes frightened by being in the company of people with dementia because they couldn't see it in themselves. Their mother's behaviour was showing us this was how she felt. My ally was Mr K, Penny's husband, who said, "You wouldn't get me in that lounge in a month of Sundays." Persuaded by their dad, the family conceded that Penny was never a challenge when away from people with dementia and therefore maybe my argument had some merit. To demonstrate my commitment to what I referred to as 'room centred care', I talked about the need to enrich Penny's room so it resonated with who she was and the life she had lived. I wanted it to feel less like a bedroom and more like a bed-sitting room where it would be a pleasure to spend your time.

As the family became caught up in my enthusiasm, one of her sons agreed the idea sounded appealing but he would not want to see the door to their mother's room closed for then he would know their mother had been shut away, if not as a punishment then clearly for the benefit of the other residents. The home manager readily agreed. I told them that to recommend that Penny spend her days in her room did not mean that she would be denied exposure to what was happening beyond her door. One of the staff's objectives would be to give Penny good reason to be out of her room, to be in the lounge or in an activity room because there was something happening she would want to be part of, not to be there simply because the physical space existed.

In many ways you can see a person's room as their home, where their care is centred, and the communal living space as their world into which people are enticed because it is a worthwhile place to be. There were smiles, nods and as satisfaction descended upon us all Mr K somewhat hesitatingly said, "But won't some of them walk in and take my wife's things? How will you stop that from happening, because we don't want her door to be closed?"

There was no question of placing a 'child gate' across the doorway for not only would it give the worst impression of degrading institutional care it would also be a hazard to every resident who unlike Penny could walk unaided. Had Penny's husband unearthed a flaw that would be impossible to resolve? We agreed that her personal integrity and possessions had to be protected. We said that 'room-centred care' inevitably required a more dynamic, out-reaching style of care wherein staff would walk the corridors and visit people in their rooms to ensure all was well. However, they were not convinced this would prevent a lost and bewildered resident walking into Penny's room. Nor were we.

Three of us sat down refusing to abandon what we saw could be the solution to Penny's distress. To this day I am not sure who suggested it first: me, the home manager or the head of care. Whoever it was, we all agreed that we might have the answer. Why not attach a beaded-curtain to the door frame? Even with the door open a beaded-curtain pulled across would not only deter someone from entering Penny's room, it probably would disguise the fact that here was an entrance to somewhere. As a result, residents would simply walk past. We talked the idea over with some of the staff and one of the care assistants raised a concern. What if a resident tried to walk through, might they not get tangled and "strangle themselves"? While improbable, we could not ignore the possibility. We could not manage one risk at the price of creating another. To our relief, with time, effort and immense gratitude to the wonders of the internet we purchased a beaded curtain that would collapse if pulled and so could never be a hazard, let alone be transformed into a ligature.

Penny's family were superb. In came ornaments, photographs and all sorts of knick-knacks. Her dressing table was simply that, her dressing table with hairbrush, perfume and jewellery. We learnt that she adored musicals – West Side Story, Oklahoma, South Pacific, Seven Brides For Seven Brothers, plus Elvis Presley and Grease were on her list of favourites – so a portable TV, CD player and a library of videos and albums now adorned the unit by the window. Above her bed was a collage made by her granddaughter who by good fortune was studying at a nearby art college. Family past and present now smiled down on Penny. She even drank tea from her own mug, the one her son had brought back from Dublin, the one with the handle shaped like a harp. This was truly Penny's home.

As we had said, her care plan had to be active and out-reaching. Every 20 minutes she was checked on. Was all well? Was she sitting comfortably? Was her music still playing? Had the video finished? Was it time for her to sit quietly? Was there anything going on in the home that Penny might like to join in? Was anybody in her room? To the last question the answer was always no; the beaded-curtain had worked. On a few occasions some residents stopped and played with the beads but none had tried to enter Penny's room.

There was no doubt that Penny was now a contented

woman. Safe and comfortable among her familiar things, undisturbed by people who had once tormented her she no longer had reason to shout out or be spiteful. Instead she sat quietly for hours watching her films, listening to music or simply gazing around. Who knows how much of her world she understood. Probably only a little, but that did not matter. Life felt better.

Along the corridor four bedrooms away was a woman with similar fears. She experienced the same revulsion when faced with people with dementia, yet she also had been reacquainted with what it meant to have peace of mind. Nowadays she was calm and her days tranquil. Her name is Janet (see chapter six). Like Penny she hardly ever left her room and was rarely invited to do so. Surrounded by her possessions and away from those who frightened her, Janet, a shy and timid woman, was again at peace. She was once more the sister and aunt who had been cherished, and as a result her family was again there for her. Both Penny K and Janet had been restored to their previous selves by the security, reassurance and continuity provided by 'room-centred care'. Yet if their paths were to have crossed in the corridor or in the lounge enmity and recrimination would have been in the air – for both would have known that they shared absolutely nothing in common.

&

Acknowledgements

I owe a great debt to the grand pioneers who approached the complex worlds of psychology and neurology through the medium of storytelling. I particularly wish to acknowledge Sigmund Freud whose ideas today are seen by many as archaic but whose writings introduced me to the complexity of the mind; and Oliver Sacks, who illuminated my understanding of the relationship between brain and behaviour.

I wish to acknowledge the many important and creative contributions by colleagues with whom I have worked and who helped inform my ideas and inspire my faith in the capacity of the human spirit to survive in the face of adversity. I am sorry that I have had to anonymise your involvement in these stories.

Also many thanks to Andrew Chapman for his sensitive editing of the original text, and Richard Hawkins and Sue Benson at Hawker Publications for their words of encouragement and their benevolent guidance.

This book is dedicated to my wife who gave me her loving support when I really needed it and my children who made sacrifices without complaint.

APPENDIX I

Bibliography

Garland K, Beer E, Eppingstall B, O'Connor D W (2007) A comparison of two treatments of agitated behaviour in nursing home residents with dementia: simulated presence and preferred music. *American Journal of Geriatric Presence Therapy*, in press.

Gilleard C J (1984) *Living with dementia.* London: Croom Helm.

Hope RA, Fairburn C G (1990) The nature of wandering in dementia: a community based study. *International Journal of Geriatric Psychiatry* 5 239-45.

James I A, Carlsson-Mitchell P, Ellingford, J, Mackenzie L (2007) Promoting attitude change: staff training programme on continence care. *PSIGE Newsletter.*

James I, Mackenzie L, Stephenson M, Roe M (2006) Dealing with challenging behaviour through an analysis of need: the Columbo approach. In Marshall M, Allan K. (eds.) *Dementia: walking not wandering.* London: Hawker Publications.

Jones M (1999) *Gentlecare.* Vancouver: Hartley & Marks.

Keady J, Nolan M, Gilliard J (1995) Listen to the voices of experience. *Journal of Dementia Care* 3 15-17.

Killick J (1994) Giving shape to shadows. *Elderly Care* 6 10.

Kitwood T (1989) Brain, mind and dementia: with particular reference to Alzheimer's disease. *Ageing and Society* 9 1-15.

Kitwood T (1990) The dialectics of dementia: with particular reference to Alzheimer's disease. *Ageing and Society* 10 177-196.

Kitwood T (1994) Lowering our defences by playing the part. *Journal of Dementia Care* 2 12-14.

Kitwood T (1995) Cultures of care: tradition and change. In Kitwood T, Benson S (eds) *The new culture of dementia care.* London: Hawker Publications.

Koch T, Webb C (1996) The biomedical construction of ageing: implications for nursing care of older people. *Journal of Advanced Nursing* 23 954-959.

Luria A R (1976) *The working brain: an introduction to neuropsychology.* New York: Basic Books.

Marshall M (1998) Therapeutic buildings for people with dementia. In Judd S, Marshall M, Phippen P (eds) *Design for dementia.* London: Hawker Publications.

Marshall M (2006) Introduction. In Marshall M, Allan K (eds) *Dementia: walking not wandering.* London: Hawker Publications.

Moniz- Cook E, Woods R T, Richards K (2001) Functional analysis of challenging behaviour in dementia: the role of superstition. *International Journal of Geriatric Psychiatry* 16 45-56.

Moniz-Cook E, Stokes G, Agar S (2003) Difficult behaviour and dementia in nursing homes: five cases of psychosocial intervention. *Clinical Psychology and Psychotherapy* 10 197-208.

Morris E (1995) This living hand. *The New Yorker* 16 January 1995.

Morton I (1999) *Person-centred approaches to dementia care.* Bicester: Speechmark.

Pastalan L (1984) Architectural research and life space changes. In Snyder J (ed) *Architectural research.* New York: Van Nostrand Reinhold.

Peak J S, Cheston R (2002) Using simulated presence therapy with people with dementia. *Ageing and Mental Health* 6 77-81.

Rogers C R (1951) *Client-centred therapy: its current practice, implications and theory.* Boston: Houghton Mifflin.

Sacks O (1985) *The man who mistook his wife for a hat.* London: Picador.

Sacks O (2007) The Abyss. *The New Yorker* 24th September.

Samson DM, McDonnell A (1990) Functional analysis and challenging behaviours. *Behavioural Psychotherapy* 18 259-272.

Shulman K I (2000) Clock-drawing: is it the ideal cognitive screening test? *International Journal of Geriatric Psychiatry* 15 548-561.

Stokes G (1995) Incontinent or not? Person first, dementia second. *Journal of Dementia Care* 3 20-21.

Stokes G (1996) Challenging behaviour in dementia: a psychological approach. In Woods R (ed) *Clinical psychology and ageing*. Chichester: John Wiley.

Stokes G (1996) Driven by fear to defend his secure world. *Journal of Dementia Care* 4 14-16.

Stokes G (1997) Reacting to a real threat. *Journal of Dementia Care* 5 14-15.

Stokes G (2000) *Challenging Behaviour in Dementia*. Speechmark, Bicester.

Stokes G (2003) Psychological approaches to bowel care in older people with dementia. In Potter J, Norton C, Cottenden A (eds) *Bowel care in older people*. London: Royal College of Physicians.

Stokes G (2004) What have I done to deserve this? Understanding aggressive resistance. *Journal of Dementia Care* 12 30-32.

Stokes G (2006) We walk, they wander. In Marshall M, Allan K (eds) *Dementia: walking not wandering*. London: Hawker Publications.

Townsend P (1962) *The last refuge*. London: Routledge & Kegan Paul.

Wattis J (2002) Medication in the treatment of dementia. In Stokes G, Goudie F (eds) *The essential dementia care handbook*. Bicester: Speechmark.

Woods R, Ashley J (1995) Simulated presence therapy: using selected memories to manage problem behaviours in Alzheimer's disease patients. *Geriatric Nursing* 16 9-14.

APPENDIX II

Glossary

AGNOSIA – a disorder of recognition whereby what is, for example, seen has no meaning (visual agnosia). Agnosia literally means 'no knowledge'.

APRAXIA – a disturbance of learned voluntary movements (such as dressing) despite adequate physical and sensory ability. Apraxia literally means 'no work'.

ATROPHY – a wasting or decrease in the size of a body organ. Cortical atrophy refers to the loss of brain cells and the resulting shrinkage of the brain.

BARRIER NURSING – people who are suffering from contagious infections are often nursed in isolation using a procedure known as barrier nursing. These techniques protect the hospital or care environment and staff from contamination with dangerous pathogens.

BEHAVIOURAL ANALYSIS – often referred to as an ABC analysis, the methodology requires a clear description of the problem behaviour under investigation ('B') that is understood in terms of the observed influence of the events preceding it and the setting within which it occurred (antecedents 'A') and the observable consequences that followed ('C'). Behavioural analysis can be the precursor to a functional analysis.

CARE ACTIONS – the activities of care staff when looking after a person.

CARE PLAN – the actions needed and the services required to meet the health and social care needs of a client.

COMMUNITY MENTAL HEALTH TEAM – a team of NHS and social care professionals supporting people living in their homes.

COMMUNITY PSYCHIATRIC NURSE – a nurse with mental health training caring for people living in their own homes.

CONFABULATION – when memory for recent events is impaired and the person is asked what have they been doing the person may 'plug' the gap with a fiction. This is confabulation. Not an outrageous fiction but an account of how life used to be lived.

CT BRAIN SCAN – Computerized tomography is a scanning technique that images the brain.

DISINHIBITION – a neurobehavioural symptom that results from lesions within or injury to the brain, particularly to the frontal lobe. Disinhibition results in a person having a reduced capacity to manage or control their impulses in the way we all do each day for reasons of politeness or sensitivity or social appropriateness or desire to keep our true feelings hidden from others.

DOOR BAFFLES – Some doors on dementia care units and wards are controlled by digital codes or have other protective systems to discourage people with dementia from going through them.

DYSFLUENCY – impairment in the speed and ease of verbal production. It is typically measured by the quantity of words produced, usually within a restricted category and normally within a time limit.

EEG – the electroencephalograph (EEG) was one of the first ways of observing human brain activity by measuring electrical signals and patterns within the brain.

EMI UNIT – Elderly Mentally Infirm unit is a social services term for a dementia care unit.

ENDURING POWER OF ATTORNEY – in England, Wales and Northern Ireland it is a legal document whereby a person of sound mind grants authority to a named person to make decisions on their behalf concerning assets and finances in anticipation of the possibility of not being intellectually capable at some future date. The Mental Capacity Act (2005) replaced Enduring Powers of Attorney (EPA) with a new and different type of power of attorney called a Lasting Power of Attorney (LPA).

EXECUTIVE (DYS)FUNCTION – executive functions are the highest intellectual abilities that enable a person to engage successfully in independent behaviour. Executive dysfunction means there are problems with reasoning, judgement, planning and decision-making.

FUNCTIONAL ANALYSIS – the process of determining the meaning or purpose (or 'function') of a behaviour before developing an intervention.

FUNCTIONAL DISPLACEMENT – a therapeutic approach that provides a person who is behaving in a way that challenges others with an equivalent but more socially acceptable means of meeting their needs.

INCIDENTAL LEARNING – learning that occurs when stimuli are attended to without an intention to learn. In other words acquisition occurs without dedicated effort to remember.

INFANTILIZATION – treating a person with dementia patronisingly as if they were a young child. It is a feature of a malignant social psychology (see p24).

LASTING POWER OF ATTORNEY – *see* Enduring Power of Attorney.

LIFE STORY WORK – learning about a person's life and using the knowledge gained to therapeutically engage with that person.

MMSE (MINI MENTAL STATE EXAMINATION) – a brief screening measure of cognition that can reveal impairments suggestive of dementia.

PERSEVERATION – when people, usually with frontal lobe brain damage, repeat a movement or an act or activity over and over again involuntarily. It is sometimes referred to as the 'stuck needle syndrome'.

PERSON-CENTRED CARE – care plans that focus on the needs and uniqueness of people as distinct from institutionalised task-oriented cultures of care that are preoccupied with disease and disability and which hold on to a belief that all people live their lives in the same way.

PERSONHOOD – a term made popular by the late Professor Tom Kitwood, personhood is the acknowledgement by others of the presence of a person with dementia who as a unique individual is worthy of respect and whose point of view is to be valued.

PROCEDURAL MEMORY – also known as implicit memory, procedural memory is the long-term memory of skills and procedures.

PROJECTION – a defence mechanism in which one attributes to others one's own unacceptable or unwanted thoughts and emotions.

REMINISCENCE – the process of recollecting past experiences or events

REPRESSION – the exclusion of painful impulses or emotions from the conscious mind.

RISK ASSESSMENT – determining the probability or likelihood of a defined event with a specific hazardous outcome happening. It is the first step in the process of risk management.

SENSORY GARDEN – a safe and stimulating garden that appeals to all the senses with refreshing colour, scent, movement, sound and visual interest.

SEPARATION ANXIETY – a state of excessive anxiety when an individual is apart from a person or place that makes them feel safe and secure.

VISUAL ACCESS – this means that when in a building, such as a care home, people with dementia have the opportunity to see or sense where they are or where they want to go.